Radio Amateur's Guide

Radio Wave Propagation
(HF Bands)

Radio Amateur's Guide

Radio Wave Propagation
(HF Bands)

F. C. Judd G2BCX

Heinemann: London

William Heinemann Ltd
10 Upper Grosvenor Street, London W1X 9PA

LONDON   MELBOURNE   JOHANNESBURG   AUCKLAND

First published 1987
© William Heinemann 1987

British Library Cataloguing in Publication Data
Judd, F. C.
  Radio Wave Propagation
  (HF bands).
  1. Radio wave propagation
  I. Title
  621.3841'1   TK6553

ISBN 0 434 90926 2

Printed in Great Britain by
R. J. Acford Ltd, Chichester

Contents

Preface   ix

1 Discovery: the ionospheric regions

The Marconi Era   1
The Rayleigh theory of diffraction   3
Discovery of the reflecting medium   5
The early experiments   5
The early work of E. V. Appleton   7
The experiments continue   8
The E and F regions   9
Critical frequency   10
Pulse technique   10
Further observations   11
A tribute to E. V. Appleton   11
Development of the pulse technique   13
The timing of wireless echoes   14
Return to pulse sounding   16
The ionospheric regions   19
Ionization and electron density   19
The D region   20
The E region   21
The F region   21
The earth's weather and the ionosphere   21
Refraction   22
Some definitions   22
Refraction (radio waves)   22
Diffraction   24
Summary   24
References   25

2   Ionospheric region parameters

The ionosonde   27
Ionograms   31
Split echoes   34
The effect of the earth's magnetic field   37
General function of the ionospheric regions   37
Skip distance   39
Ionospheric region height and transmission distance   41
Virtual height and critical frequency   41
Maximum usable frequency   42
Lowest usable frequency   42
References   43

3   The eleven-year solar cycles and sunspot activity

The active sun and sunspots   47
Solar flares   49
Solar radio emissions   51
Sunspot numbers   51
The end of solar cycle no. 21   54
Changing conditions during eleven-year cycles   54
Prediction of the end of solar cycle no. 2 and the
beginning of cycle no. 22 DX predictions   57
The solar cycle and critical frequency   58
Ionospheric region variations   61
Ionized reflecting media   61
The origin of the sunspot numbers   63
Sunspot count information   65
References   66

4   Ionospheric anomalies

Trans-equatorial openings   68
Polarization and direction of travel   68
Great circle paths   68
Spurious directivity   69
One-way propagation paths   69
Fading   70
Ionization changes   70
Scatter propagation   71

More about sporadic E   73
Meteor trails   75
Aurorae (borealis and australis)   75
Ionospheric storms   77
Sudden ionospheric disturbances (SID)   77
N and M modes of propagation   77
Other ionospheric and solar cycle events   79
References   82

5   Ionospheric radar systems

The American OTHR system   83
The development of OTHR   84
How OTHR operates   85
Normal mode of operation   86
Interrogate mode   89
Interleaved mode   90
Frequency range   90
Radar functions   90
Transmitting aerial system   91
The transmitters   92
The receive function   92
The operations functions   93
OTHR tracking   94
OTHR coverage and the ionosphere   95
The Russian system   97
Analysis of 'Woodpecker' signals   98
Interference to amateur radio   100
Coded information   102
British OTHR system   103
References   104

6   The transmitting aerial and propagation

Reflection from the ground   105
The aerial image   108
Ground reflection factor   110
Angles and incidence   112
Omni-directional ionospheric propagation   114
Assessing ionospheric conditions   117

Chordal mode propagation   117
Ionospheric propagation with vertical aerials   118
References   119

7 Radio waves: radiation

Radio wave radiation   120
Wavelength and phase   122
Field strength   124
Attenuation   124
Polarization   124
Ground-wave propagation   125
The surface wave   125
The space wave   126
Propagation from vertical aerials   126
Conclusion   127
References   128

8 Ionospheric (F region) propagation data

Instruction for use   129
Sporadic E (Es) data   134
Questions and answers data   138
End of solar cycle no. 21   143

Index   145

Preface

World-wide radio communication on the amateur radio bands ranging from 1.8 to nearly 30 MHz, as well as the short-wave broadcast bands, is achieved almost entirely by ionospheric propagation, more loosely termed by most as 'sky-wave' propagation.

Ionospheric radio wave propagation is a subject not completely understood by all radio amateurs and short-wave listeners, although most are aware of the fact that, if the ionospheric regions were non-existent, long-distance radio communication would not be possible, unless accomplished entirely by satellites.

This mode of radio propagation is very closely linked with the so-called 11-year solar sunspot cycles to which a chapter of this book has been devoted. There is also a chapter that deals entirely with ionospheric radar systems, one of which is well known to radio amateurs and SWLs the world over as the 'Woodpecker', about which little information has previously been published.

The main contents of the book stem not only from some fifty years or so of active operation on the allocated HF bands as a licensed radio amateur but also from an intensive study of the subject, and daily 'ionospheric' region observations covering a period of more than three years. From the considerable amount of valuable information obtained from these observations, some has been included to highlight specific aspects of ionospheric parameters and anomalies.

Although the subject as a whole may seem a little complex, I have attempted to simplify it as much as possible without detracting from the technicalities involved and at the same time include as much usable data for the radio amateur and short-wave listeners alike. This includes a short chapter on ground-wave propagation as well as information concerned with transmitting aerials.

I am also indebted to the following authoritative sources for specific information, data concerned with ionospheric parameters and photographs, etc. These include the Rutherford Appleton Laboratory (World Data Centre) in Oxfordshire, The Royal Belgian Observatory, Brussels, the USA Department of Commerce (Atmospheric Administration), Boulder, Colorado, the USA Department of Defense (Electronics Division), Massachusetts, and Marconi Radar Systems Ltd of Chelmsford, Essex. References to other sources of information are given at the end of each chapter.

F. C. Judd (G2BCX)
Norfolk, 1987

1 Discovery: the ionospheric regions

The ionosphere, as we know today, consists of layers or regions of rarefied air, and when certain conditions prevail, one or the other of these regions can become a very efficient reflector of radio waves. The frequency spectrum over which reflection and/or refraction can occur is very wide and includes the range from around 1 MHz to over 30 MHz, thus embracing the amateur HF bands and the short-wave broadcasts bands. Ionospheric radio wave propagation may sometimes extend into the VHF spectrum when a particular event known as 'sporadic E' occurs. The ionospheric regions were only discovered about 80 years ago, after G. Marconi first spanned the Atlantic Ocean with 'wireless' waves, although he was uncertain as to how these waves could travel in such a way as to follow the curvature of the earth. His feat in transmitting wireless signals from England and receiving them on the other side of the Atlantic, was in fact queried. Did it really happen? There was only Marconi's and Kemp's own confirmation that the signals had been received at St John's, Newfoundland from the transmitter in England, located at Poldhu in Cornwall. Nevertheless, an announcement appeared in *The Times* newspaper on 16 December 1901, confirming that Marconi's 'electrical signals' had been received and that the achievement rated an importance that was impossible to over-value. So the question remained. Did Marconi's transmissions follow the curved surface of the earth, or were they propagated by a natural reflecting medium of some kind located in the earth's upper atmosphere? Lord Rayleigh suggested this was not possible, but he was proved wrong.

One very notable development by G. Marconi is worth recalling, and this concerns what he called 'directional aerials'. The term 'directional' can apply to an aerial that radiates equally

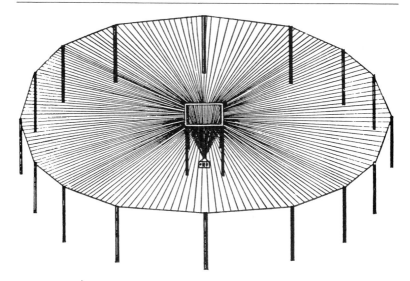

Figure 1   *Aerial used by G. Marconi at Glace Bay, Nova Scotia in connection with his first transatlantic wireless transmissions (see text)*

in all directions around it, but it is then said to be 'omni-directional'. By 1905 Marconi had an entirely new aerial erected at Glace Bay in Nova Scotia with a view to increasing wireless communication distances still further. This aerial is illustrated in Figure 1 and was probably omni-directional. It consisted of an 'umbrella' of wires, 200 in all, supported by four masts at the centre, from which the wires ran out laterally to two concentric rings of masts, each 180 feet high, with eight in an inner circle (not shown in the drawing) and sixteen for an outer circle. Provision was made to increase the diameter of the 'umbrella' section by using another outer circle of forty-eight masts each 50 feet high. The diameter of the aerial without the extension was 2200 feet.

Results with this enormous aerial were extremely satisfying, with reception during daylight hours up to 1800 miles. Was this significant? Apparently not, at least not at that time, but now the 'daylight' range confirms that the mode of propagation over such long distances was in fact via the then undiscovered ionospheric regions. It was not long, however, before various theories were put forward to explain why wireless waves could be propagated over great distances, although no definite conclusion was reached until Oliver Heaviside in England and A. E. Kennelly in America, suggested that there must be a 'reflecting' medium in the upper atmosphere that caused the waves to be returned to earth at considerable distances from the transmitter. This being true, it meant that except for very short distances, covered by what we now refer to as ground-wave propagation, wireless waves did *not* follow the curvature of the earth's surface.

The Rayleigh theory of diffraction

Theorizing about the existence of a reflecting region somewhere above the earth's normal atmosphere was one thing but proving it by getting up there was another. Space probes had not been invented but were probably thought about. Otherwise there was no way of getting up to wherever 'there' happened to be.

At least one scientist, Lord Rayleigh, stated that while radio waves, like light waves, could be diffracted, i.e. bent round a sharp edge or curved surface, the bending was insufficient to account for the long-distance transmissions that were being experienced. The bending of light (wavelength 5×10^{-5} cm) was insufficient to diffract round a sphere of 3 cm radius (see Figure 2). Scaled up pro-rata, a radio wave of 100 metres (wavelength) would not diffract round the curvature of the earth. At higher frequencies (shorter wavelengths), radiation will travel for a short distance along the surface but will not otherwise diffract. The higher the frequency the less the defraction. (G. Marconi's transmissions were in the region of 300 to 400 metres although shorter wavelengths were used later.)

With amateur radio this effect is quite noticeable in that stations fairly close to each other will be able to exchange good signals. (This is usually referred to as 'ground-wave' propagation.) Otherwise transmission and reception is via one of the ionospheric regions depending on the frequency in use.

It is interesting to note that very long wave transmissions will diffract round the surface of the earth but that does not really concern us here.

Lord Rayleigh's theory of diffraction is worth remembering for reasons that will be apparent later but it does illustrate that without some intervening reflecting medium around a sphere, radiation from a source very close to the surface would simply travel on into the space surrounding the sphere (with the exception of very long wavelength radiation).

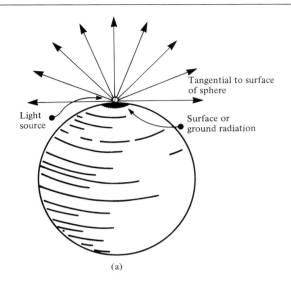

(a)

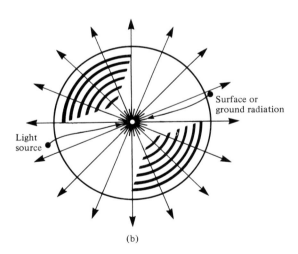

(b)

Figure 2 *Illustration of Lord Rayleigh's theory as described in text. (a) Source of light at some point on a sphere with a radius of 3 cm and showing the directions of radiation in the 'vertical' plane. (b) Radiation in the horizontal plane. Note small amount of radiation along the surface due to diffraction*

Discovery of the reflecting medium

It was by about 1902 that Heaviside and Kennelly reached the conclusion that a 'conducting layer' of some kind was the medium that 'guided' wireless waves around the earth, and although this became known as 'the Heaviside layer', its actual existence was not proven by positive tests and investigation until much later. Nevertheless, the idea had stimulated the minds of other scientists, notably Professor E. V. Appleton in England and G. Breit and M. A. Tuve in America.

It was not until 1925 that its existence was experimentally verified beyond reasonable doubt. In that year several independent methods of measuring ionospheric heights were published and/or used, the most notable being those employed by Appleton, Barnett, Breit and Tuve. Prior to Kennelly and Heaviside, the idea of an upper atmospheric conducting layer was also speculated upon by geomagneticians, e.g. Gauss and Balfour, and proof of a downcoming abnormally polarized wave was given by Eckersley in 1921.

There have been at least four phases in the development of long-distance radio communication that have stimulated the science of ionospheric measurement. One, already mentioned, was that of G. Marconi's success in spanning the Atlantic with 'wireless waves' in 1901, the development of radio direction finding during the First World War, Anglo-Australian short-wave radio communication with low power in 1924, and the growth of medium frequency broadcasting after 1922.

The early experiments

The year 1925 is probably the most notable in the history of experimental investigation into the propagation of radio waves. Three important experiments were carried out to test the theory that a conducting medium existed in or above the normal atmosphere and that this was indeed responsible for propagating radio waves over great distances. In brief, these experiments were as follows:

1 An experiment in wave interference which proved that while the steady signal received form a medium frequency transmission during the day was due to a direct wave, at night the signal was subject to fading and was found to include an

additional 'indirect wave' (from the same transmission source) but which had taken a longer path.

2   Verification of the existence (of a conducting region) by employing radio waves in the form of pulses of short duration. This technique separated the direct and indirect waves and proved that, whilst a direct pulse was received during the day, additional 'echoes' were present at night.

3   Another experiment proved that the indirect wave was not laterally deviated on the surface of the earth but incident at the receiver at an appreciable downcoming angle.

It was clear however, that logical proof of the existence of a reflecting region in the upper atmosphere required more than one of these experimental observations.

It may of course seem strange that long-distance radio communication had existed for almost a quarter of a century before absolute proof was established of what we now accept without question, and know as 'ionospheric propagation', and yet at one time the existence of a radio reflecting medium above the surface of the earth was strongly denied in England (1915) and later in Germany (1924). By March 1925, Smith-Rose and Barfield of the National Physical Laboratory, were compelled to admit that their own observations in connection with downcoming waves, returned from the upper atmosphere, could not be accepted as evidence, for or against.

This now leads us to two papers with rather forthright titles, both published in 1925, but which undoubtedly put the 'radio cat' among the 'no-ionospheric pigeons'. It is the outcome of the contents of these two papers that we shall later be concerned with. They were:

(a)   *On Some Direct Evidence for Downward Atmospheric Reflection of Electric Rays* by E. V. Appleton and M. A. F. Barnett (England).

(b)   *A Test of the Existence of the Conducting Layer* by G. Breit and M. A. Tuve (USA).

The first paper described the results obtained with the 'phase' or frequency change method of measuring the path-length of an indirect wave, whilst the second dealt with the observation of radio 'echoes' using the pulse transmission technique. The outcome of both provided the basis on which our present-day knowledge of the ionosphere and also radar was founded.

The early work of E. V. Appleton

During 1924 Professor E. V. Appleton's interest was centred on several fields of research, one of the most notable being the propagation of radio waves.

However, in April 1924, Miles Barnet arrived in England from New Zealand with the intention of working with Appleton on 'wireless wave' propagation. Before this time, in 1922, the BBC had set up the medium wave London broadcasting station known in those days by its callsign as 2LO. Barnett set to work first by recording the signal strength of signals from 2LO received in Cambridge. He found that during the day the signals were almost constant but at nightfall began to vary in strength. The variation was referred to as 'fading'.

Appleton and Barnett, now working together, assumed that the Kennelly-Heaviside layer was responsible for this night-time fading, an assumption which later proved to be correct. They eventually came to the conclusion that during the day the waves reached the receiver by a ground path only, but at night reflected waves arrived in addition to this but were received simultaneously. When the waves arrived 'in phase' they added and when in 'anti-phase' they subtracted. It was considered that, if the path difference (D), as in Figure 3, between that of the ground-

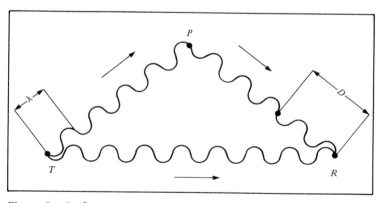

Figure 3   *Radio waves arriving at a receiving point (R) from a transmitter (T) via two different paths. If the indirect path (TPR) is longer or shorter by a half-wavelength with reference to the direct path (TR), then phase cancellation of the total received signals will occur. If the paths (TPR) and (TR) are each a whole number (n) of wavelengths, both the direct and indirect signals from (T) will arrive at (R) in phase*

wave and that of the reflected wave was a whole number (n) of wavelengths, the waves would add. If it was a whole number plus or minus a half-wavelength, then they would subtract. It was also noticed that the extent of the fading increased after sunset and that the strength of the reflected wave increased as darkness approached.

Both Appleton and Barnett concluded that further experimentation was needed to prove that those experiments already carried out were valid. Accordingly, arrangements were made on 11 December 1924 to use the BBC transmitter at Bournemouth, and receiving equipment sited at Oxford, to carry out an experiment that involved changing the wavelength. This revealed the fact that the height of the reflecting medium was about 100 kilometres. As we know now, this is the average height of the E region and of sporadic E cloud formation.

On the basis of such an encouraging result, Appleton now concentrated his energies on finding out more about the constitution of the upper atmosphere. The term 'ionosphere' had not at this time been used. He also realized that 'atmospherics' (in connection with radio waves) offered the possibilities of investigation into another of the fundamental aspects of nature.

At this stage however, he left Cambridge to become Wheatstone Professor of Physics at Kings College in London, and was able to use a transmitter set up at the National Physical Laboratory at Teddington and a receiver located at Peterborough. The main investigations now were how the height of the reflecting medium and the strength of the reflected wave varied around the period of dawn.

He found that both the height and strength decreased as the radiation from the sun built up the ionization, so the experiments usually stopped about an hour after sunrise when the 'sky-wave' became too weak to be of any use.

The experiments continue

In 1927 an eclipse of the sun that occurred just after sunrise provided a unique way of proving that the height of the Heaviside layer changed, which it did, just at the time of the eclipse. This observation was important as it also suggested that ionization of the layer was being produced by radiation that travelled from the sun to earth at the speed of light.

Whilst the various experiments were being made, Appleton was also thinking about how the waves were reflected and what else he could find out about ionization. First he modified an earlier theory (Lorentz) to show how the earth's magnetic field could affect the radio waves through a process of 'double refraction'. He called this the 'magneto-ionic' theory and the equation for the refractive index became known as the Appleton-Hartree equation which fully describes all aspects of ionospheric radio wave propagation.

Some time later a new phenomenon was noticed. Employing the pulsed radio wave technique, observations revealed what was at first thought to be double reflection, i.e. pulses travelling up to the layer and down, and then up and down again. However, continued investigation proved that this was *not* a double reflection from a single layer but an additional reflection from another layer at much greater height.

The E and F regions

When E. V. Appleton discovered the existence of another reflecting layer he may not have immediately realized that this would become the medium for communication by radio over even greater distances, though it is doubtful whether the fact escaped him for very long. This new layer was soon to be of major interest to radio amateurs and professional radio communication companies the world over.

Appleton called it the 'F' layer (or upper layer) although it was also known as the 'Appleton layer'. The lower one, known mainly as the Heaviside layer, he designated the 'E' layer. Use of the letters E and F arose in an interesting way. In his early calculations concerning waves reflected from the Heaviside layer, Appleton used the letter E to denote the electric field of the wave. When he wanted to calculate the effects of two waves, one from each layer, he denoted the second field by using the letter F. It was later that the layers were formerly designated with the letters E and F for the lower and upper layers respectively. The letters A, B, C and D may possibly have been held in reserve in the event that other ionospheric layers might be discovered, e.g. the D region (or layer).

Now that the E layer had been penetrated, Appleton's attention was directed toward finding out why. First a shorter wavelength was employed (100 metres) and reflections from the new F layer were observed most of the night. However, he also found that with the shorter wavelength, reflections from the F layer were stronger during the daytime and that, for the first time, observations could be carried out during daylight hours. The relationship between the F layer and short-wave radio will become even more apparent in the following chapters.

Critical frequency

After the foregoing discovery Appleton realized that measurement of the 'critical penetration frequency' was possible. This is a frequency that would just penetrate the E layer and provide a measure of the maximum electron density in that layer. Arrangements were therefore made to carry out a 'wave change' experiment using a series of different mean wavelengths to determine which would penetrate the layer and which would not. Although these experiments were time consuming, Appleton wrote, in 1931, it had been possible to make one determination of the critical frequency in each hour and by this method it could be shown that the electron density varied with the height of the sun above the horizon. The reader may be interested to know that critical frequency as well as E and F layer heights are measured hourly in every 24 hours at the Rutherford Appleton Ionosonde stations at Slough in Middlesex and South Uist in the Hebrides. Some examples of these measurements will be found elsewhere in the book.

Pulse technique

As the wavelength change method employed earlier was too slow, Appleton continued to use the pulse technique originally devised and used by Breit and Tuve in America. With this method, short pulses of radio waves from a transmitter were timed for the journey to one or the other layers and back to earth so that the height of the layer, or more correctly the virtual height from which reflection takes place, could be measured.

In 1926 Watson-Watt had made the suggestion that this conducting region above the earth's normal atmosphere should be called 'the ionosphere'.

By 1932 the science of ionospheric physics was well established and using the pulse technique over a wide range of frequencies, Appleton rapidly accumulated data concerned with how the ionosphere changed with the time of day (and night), the seasons of the year, and the solar cycle of approximately eleven years duration.

Further observations

From 1932, which had been declared a 'polar year' and onwards, Appleton continued with his experimental work, delving into numerous aspects of ionospheric radio wave propagation. For example, he had expected his measurements of the ionosphere to reveal something of the 'atmospheric dynamo' theory of geomagnetism and electrical currents flowing in the high atmosphere. Later he started an experiment at Cambridge to see whether lunar effects could be detected if the height of the E layer were measured very accurately. In 1938 he was appointed Secretary of the Department of Scientific and Industrial Research, and from then on had little or no opportunity to work with research teams. Despite his responsibilities with the DISR and later with the Edinburgh University, he maintained a deep interest in ionospherics. It is said that he always carried a little book in which he made notes from time to time, the majority of which were concerned with problems in ionospheric physics.

When Appleton moved to Edinburgh he began an analysis of ionospheric data from laboratories all over the world and from which, among other things, he discovered that the ionospheric F region was greatly affected by the earth's magnetic field. From 1934 to 1952 he was President of The International Union of Scientific Radio which he recognized as a valuable organization for stimulating world-wide interest in ionospherics.

A tribute to E. V. Appleton (see Figure 4)

Whilst not forgetting all the other scientists who made valuable contributions to our present-day knowledge of ionospheric radio wave propagation, the greater part of that knowledge is due to the late Sir Edward Appleton, a Yorkshireman born in Bradford in 1892 who, after an unusually promising school career, went to St

Figure 4   *E. V. Appleton, FRS, Noble Laureate*

Johns College, Cambridge. There he read for the natural sciences
tripos and in 1914 was awarded a first class in physics. Shortly
after he volunteered for service in the Army, as the First World
War had begun, and joined the Royal Engineers as a signals
officer. At about this time the thermionic valve had been
invented, and when he eventually returned to the Cavendish
Laboratory in Cambridge in 1919 began investigations into ways
in which the valve could be used as a non-linear element in radio
circuitry. Much of this work was carried out in collaboration with
another of the early pioneers in 'wireless', namely Van der Pol.
Yet another subject that aroused Appleton's interest in 'natural
phenomenon' was 'wireless atmospherics' which, as we all know
only too well, originate from lightning and other electrical
discharges associated with certain weather conditions.

  At one time he supervised much of the work at the Radio

Research Station at Slough. It was from here and the National Physical Laboratory that Watson-Watt and others went to Orfordness in Suffolk to carry out experiments and development in the detection of aircraft approaching the British coast and which led to the establishment of the first radar stations known as CH. The initials stood for 'chain home' and a number of these stations were operational before the commencement of the Second World War.

Development of the pulse technique

Early experiments with the short radio pulse technique by Breit and Tuve indicated that the system had very promising possibilities, but there were discrepancies in the results obtained by this method and that used by Appleton. The layer heights obtained did not agree. It was soon realized however, that the method could be greatly improved by reducing the duration of the pulse thus producing better separation between the direct and indirect signals at the receiver. Early pulse measurements relied on relatively simple modulation circuitry, for example an audio frequency voltage applied to the grid of an RF amplifier in series with the usual bias voltage. Later an improved modulation system was employed using a modified Abraham-Bloch multi-vibrator which could produce pulses of less than a quarter of a millisecond duration. The time interval between pulses could be varied as required. Since the 'echo' time was not likely to be much less than one millisecond, complete separation was possible between the transmitted (ground) pulse and echo signals as displayed on a CRT time trace.

A later development made it possible to produce pulses of about 100-microsecond duration and with a repetition rate of 50 per second. An analysis of results obtained with this later system is illustrated in Figure 5. Complete separation was obtained between the ground pulse (G) and the various indirect echo signals. For example, the signal E1 is a single reflected echo from the E region at a height of about 100 kilometres and F1 is a similar echo from the F region at a height of more than 200 kilometres. Those marked F2 and F3 etc. are double and triple reflections and higher order echoes from the same region. *Note.* Multiple echoes from ionospheric regions are now designated 1E, 2E etc. and/or 1F, 2F, 3F etc., in order to distinguish them from the normal region

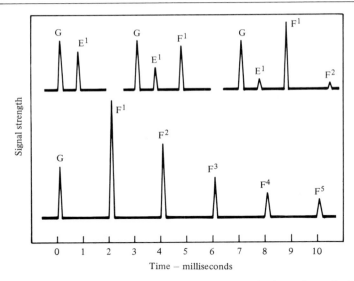

Figure 5   *Results obtained by Breit and Tuve with the pulse technique. Complete separation could be obtained between the transmitted pulse and the 'echo' pulses which enabled the virtual height of an ionospheric region to be verified with a reasonable degree of accuracy.* (AWA Technical Review, 1946, No. 2, Vol. 7)

designations of E, F1, and F2. In ionospheric sounding it is not unusual to receive four or five multiples from an intensely ionized E or F region. Some photographic examples will be shown later.

The timing of wireless echoes

This chapter would not be complete without a few words from E. V. Appleton himself, taken from one of his own articles published in the *Wireless World* dated 7 January 1931. He begins the article by referring to the 'peculiar phenomenon' associated with wireless waves travelling from one point to another by more than one route and the fact that some arrive at the point of reception a short time after those constituting the 'direct wave'. Continuing in his own words:

'As it is not possible to follow these "echo" waves in their circuitous journey, we have to infer where they have been by measuring the time they have taken in travelling. The problem is somewhat similar to that of estimating how long a journey a traveller has made on a train journey when the time taken on the journey and the average speed are known. In the wireless case we are able to observe the times at which these vagrant waves start out and arrive and thus find the time they have taken for the journey; we also know their speed through the air, and from their strength or weakness at the end of the journey we can make deductions as to the kind of time they have had on the way. It sometimes happens that the waves which have made a particularly difficult journey are so distorted on arrival as to be almost unrecognisable, so that in justice to our railways, we must admit that the analogy with the railway traveller breaks down somewhat. One of the most frequent forms of distortion is that in wireless waves sent out and travelling in a normal erect fashion, are found to arrive travelling in a horizontal recumbent position, their bodies, as it were, having been twisted through a right angle. Again we must gratefully admit that our railway analogy has broken down.'

(How delightfully simple coming from such an eminent Professor of Physics, but let E.V.A. continue.)

'In estimating the extra path traversed by the echo waves we multiply the echo time by the velocity of light. But as it happens the echo times dealt with in this article are quite short. It is useful to take a thousandth of a second (i.e. one millisecond) as our unit of time and remember that electric waves travel at 300 kilometres or 186 miles in one millisecond. For example, if the echo wave were received one millisecond after the ground signal it would mean that the echo signal had travelled 300 kilometres further than the ground waves.'

Professor Appleton then goes on to compare his timing method with those carried out in America and sets down very good reasons as to why his method proved more accurate. He concluded his article with what was then a hypothesis, that not one but two reflecting regions existed. On this too he was proved to be correct. It was not until sometime later that the vertical incidence ionospheric radio pulse sounding system was used universally, and still is today, as we shall see.

The author apologizes if some parts of this chapter have appeared to be repetitive, but this has served to correlate specific information obtained from numerous other sources.

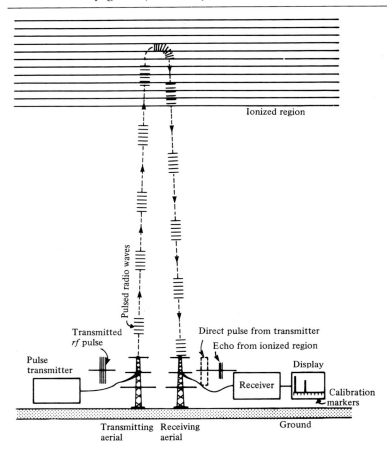

Figure 6 *Principle of transmitting 'pulsed' radio waves vertically to an ionospheric region and receiving the 'reflected' echoes (see text)*

Return to pulse sounding

The pulse technique already described is still in use today and functions on a 'straight up and straight down' basis. The pulses are transmitted vertically at an angle 90 degrees to the earth's surface. On reaching the ionospheric region they are 'reflected' back to earth and received by the same aerial, or one very close to it as in Figure 6. The pulse method does not provide a measure of true height to the base of the region but an effective or 'virtual height', since the pulse must penetrate some way into the layer before being turned around for its return journey to earth.

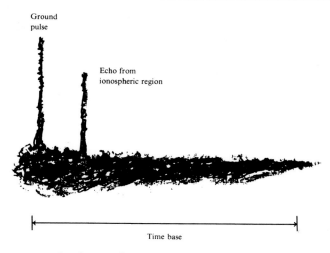

Ground
pulse

Echo from
ionospheric region

Time base

Figure 7   *Result of an early experiment by E. V. Appleton with pulsed radio-wave sounding for determining the height of an ionospheric region*

On the other hand if a wave arrives 'obliquely' at an ionospheric region, with ionization density increasing toward its upper portion, the wave front begins to slow down as it enters the region. At the peak of the turn-round it becomes stationary for an instant of time, is then transposed, after which it travels more rapidly and leaves the layer at an angle equal to that at which it arrived and at the normal speed of radio waves in free space. In short, the wave is *refracted*. A more detailed explanation is given later.

The earlier pulse transmitters delivered a peak power of a few hundred watts with a low PRF and a pulse width of around 0.5 milliseconds (usually variable). The transmitting aerial was designed to provide maximum radiation directed vertically. The receiving equipment would have been a fairly conventional superhet with reasonably good selectivity and with the output from the detector fed via a suitable amplifier to a cathode ray tube with a calibrated timebase. An early experimental result with pulse sounding by E. V. Appleton, is illustrated in Figure 7. The rather poor quality of reproduction may be due to the original photography and the fact that the example had to be copied from a printed version. The photographs in Figure 8, taken very recently, show (a) an echo from the F region, as it appeared on a

17

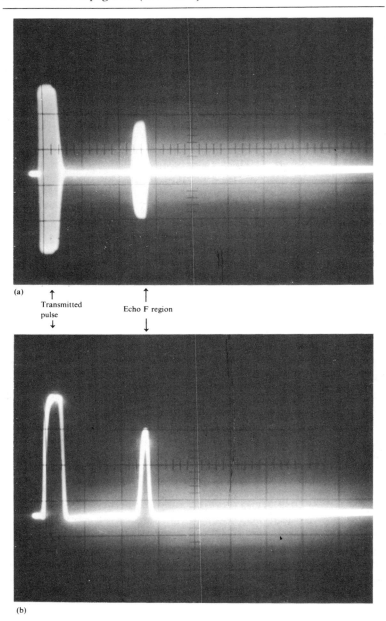

(a)

↑
Transmitted
pulse
↓

↑
Echo F region
↓

(b)

Figure 8 *(a) Echo from F region in RF form from receiver intermediate frequency output stage, before rectification. CRT display and modern equipment. (b) Same echo after rectification and limiting*

CRT, connected at the receiver intermediate frequency output stage and before rectification. Figure 8(b) shows the same echo, also with the transmitted pulse, after rectification and limiting. Narrow pulse markers for 'height' measurement are normally included in such displays.

The ionospheric regions

We have delved into some of the history of ionospherics and the work of the pioneers in this field. It is now time to take a closer look at the different regions and see how they relate to long-distance short-wave radio communication, with particular emphasis on the amateur radio HF bands. At the time of writing ionospheric radio wave propagation on the higher frequency bands e.g. 14 MHz and above, was generally poor. This was because the solar sunspot cycle (no. 21) was almost at its minimum, resulting in low sunspot counts, lower levels of radiation from the sun and therefore low ionospheric region electron densities, including the all important F region (more information in Chapter 3).

The conditions described above normally prevail during any solar cycle minimum which occurs once in approximately every eleven years. Following a solar cycle minimum, conditions on the higher frequency amateur bands become increasingly reliable for long-distance communication. This period covers the approximate time to the peak of solar cycle no. 22, although reasonably good 'DX conditions' will prevail for a year or two beyond the time of the peak. (See also Chapter 3.)

Ionization and electron density

Ionization in the upper atmosphere results from bombardment of the gases by solar radiation (ultra-violet) and creates a mixture of free electrons and positive ions. The electron density is low at high altitudes, because of the rarity of gases but lower down the density of atmospheric gases is greater and the electron density increases correspondingly. However, at even lower altitudes and where the gas density is greater still, the radiation that produces ionization has become weaker because of absorption, so the electron density is decreased.

19

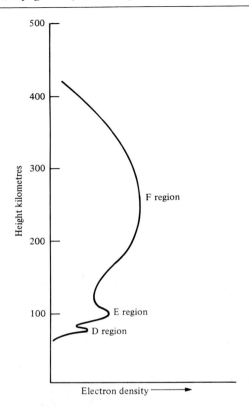

Figure 9   *Relative electron density of the three main regions (layers) D, E, and F*

The relative electron density of the three main ionospheric regions or layers (D, E and F) is shown in Figure 9, whilst Figure 10 shows how this is subject to changes by day and night.

The D region

This forms at heights above earth of between about 60 and 90 kilometres but because of the low altitude the gas density is high, and recombination between electrons and positive ions is very rapid at sunset. The D region only exists during daylight hours and because the electron density is not high, radio waves at medium and high frequencies are not reflected. On the other hand a strongly ionized D region will absorb upward and downward travelling high frequency waves.

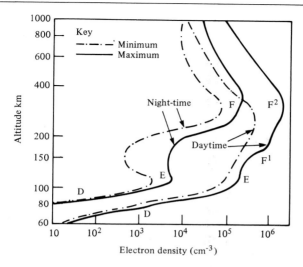

Figure 10   *Ionospheric regions (D, E and F) electron density is subject to changes during the day and night*

The E region

At heights between 100 and 125 kilometres, we have the E region with a somewhat higher electron density. The ionization in this region largely disappears at night, although not completely, and it is this region that reflects (or refracts) medium wave transmissions when the D region absorption ceases at nightfall.

The F region

The remaining regions F1 and F2, are normally referred to collectively as the F region. During periods of low ionization F2 merges with F1 which becomes the effective reflecting region F. This varies in virtual height between about 200 and 400 kilometres, or higher, depending on time of day or season. Although the electron density may be high during the daytime, it decreases at night but can still remain high enough for propagation of high frequency waves.

The earth's weather and the ionosphere

So far as is known, normal earth weather conditions do not affect the ionospheric regions although some investigators have claimed that certain ionospheric conditions and variations in the eleven-year solar cycles coincide with particular kinds of weather, a subject that is raised purely out of interest in Chapter 3.

Refraction

This is a very important aspect of ionospheric radio wave propagation but one which is difficult to illustrate without resorting to somewhat complicated diagrams. The process can, however, be explained, but it should be borne in mind that the illustrations related to this show only a single dimension.

The refraction of radio waves by an ionized region is analogous in many respects to the refraction of light waves leaving one medium (air) and entering another (water). A simple demonstration of this is to take a thin straight rod and dip it into water at an angle other than vertical. At the point where the rod meets the surface of the water it appears to bend with the rest of it, below the water, visible at a seemingly different angle to the section of rod above.

Some definitions

Refractive index of a medium. The ratio of the sine of the angle of incidence to the sine of the angle of refraction when light is refracted from a vacuum (or close approximation, namely, air) into the medium. This is equivalent to the fundamental definition: the ratio of the velocity of light in free space to that in the medium.

Angle of incidence is the angle that a line or beam of radiation makes with a line perpendicular to the surface at the point of incidence.

Angle of refraction is the angle that a refracted beam of radiation makes with the normal to the surface between two media at the point of refraction.

Refraction (radio waves)

The refractive index of an ionized region is greater than unity and increases as the electron density increases. The wavefront of an

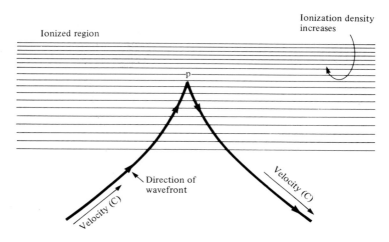

Figure 11   *Refraction. Path of a radio wavefront through an ionized region having a refractive index that increases as the electron density increases (see text)*

incident radio wave therefore starts to move in a direction closer to vertical after entering an ionized region. This movement gradually increases as the wavefront penetrates further into the region.

The 'direction' of the wavefront is illustrated in Figure 11 (large arrows) first approaching the boundary at a velocity (c) of 300×10^6 metres per second, the speed of radio waves in air. As the wavefront enters the region its velocity starts to decrease and continues to do so as it travels toward the point (p) at which the velocity reaches zero whereupon the wavefront reverses direction and the velocity begins to increase. The wavefront eventually leaves the region, its angle of exit being equal to the angle of incidence i.e. the angle at which the wavefront arrived in the first instance. The velocity on exit is restored to that of the approach velocity of 300×10^6 metres/second.

Note that the wavefront is perpendicular to the line of direction, its leading edge being the first part to enter the region and the last to leave and whereas it was uppermost on entry, it becomes lowermost on exit.

Special reference: 'Ionospheric Refraction' by Dr L. W. Brown and F. C. Judd, *Practical Wireless*, Dec. 1986.

Diffraction

Definition: When a beam of light passes through an aperture, or past the edge of an opaque obstacle and is allowed to fall upon a screen, patterns of light and dark bands (with monochromatic light), or coloured bands (with white light) are observed near the edges of the beam and extend into the geometrical shadow. This phenomenon, which is a particular case of interference, is due to the 'wave' nature of light and is known as diffraction. This is common to ALL wave motions, including radio waves.

Again, the radio wave has another counterpart in optics, and since diffraction becomes greater as the wavelength increases, it assumes some importance at radio frequencies. With radio waves travelling in a straight line (parallel to ground) one might expect that no signals would be picked up on the far side of a high hill, but in fact the bending caused by diffraction can produce a signal on the other side, in the 'shadow' area. At high frequencies a diffracted transmission would not be very strong and could be masked by other transmissions reaching the same place by another route, e.g. a direct signal (line-of-sight) or one arriving by reflection, or refraction from an ionospheric region.

The foregoing may have indicated that diffraction frequently plays a part in 'ground-wave' propagation, which it does (see Chapter 7).

Summary

This chapter has covered, albeit briefly, some of the historical facts concerned with the discovery of the ionospheric regions and the more general aspects of these relative to radio propagation at high frequencies. Some repetition of information is not totally avoidable and may even assist the reader in some instances, e.g. the necessity of not having to turn back the pages for some specific item of information.

There is much more to the subject of ionospheric radio wave propagation, particularly so from a more practical point of view, as will be discovered with further reading. Before reaching this stage however, the day-to-day measurement of ionospheric parameters will be dealt with, as well as the so-called eleven-year solar cycles and sunspot counts. Both subjects will provide even more insight into ionospherics. There are also certain anomalies associated with this mode of radio wave propagation, some of which are due to the activity of the sun, and others because of the influence of the earth's magnetic field.

Ionospheric propagation conditions are not 100 per cent predictable, nor are the solar cycles and sunspot counts, although reasonably close approximation is possible in both cases.

Transmitting/receiving aerials, as every radio amateur is well aware, play an equally important part in long distance HF bands operation, but there are some very desirable requirements here that may not be appreciated. These have not been forgotten and a later chapter has been devoted to them.

References

1 *A History of the Marconi Company*, W. J. Baker (Methuen 1970).
2 'The Early Work of G. Marconi', *Practical Wireless*, F. C. Judd, May 1984.
3 'Appleton as a Radio Scientist', *Electronics and Power*, J. A. Ratcliffe, Feb. 1966.
4 'The Timing of Wireless Echoes', *Wireless World*, Prof. E. V. Appleton, Jan. 1931.
5 'Radio Wave Propagation', *Practical Wireless*, F. C. Judd (series of articles from Jan. 1985.)
6 'Early History of the Ionosphere', *A.W.A. Technical Review*, A. L. Green, Vol. 7, No. 2, 1946.

2 Ionospheric region parameters

The principle of ionospheric region virtual height finding, arising from the pulsed radio wave technique developed by the American scientists, Breit and Tuve, and later used by E. V. Appleton, was explained in Chapter 1. Although any single transmitting/receiving frequency can be used, rather like a one-frequency radar system, it would prove somewhat tedious and time consuming to start from some specific frequency and make incremental adjustments upward in order to cover a wide range, e.g. from 1 MHz to 20 MHz. A wide frequency coverage is necessary to cater for (a) specific frequency ranges for the E and F regions and (b) to find out at which frequency reflection ceases at the onset of the critical frequency. Hence the use of a 'frequency scanning' method, keeping the transmitter and receiver tuning synchronized.

The fiftieth anniversary of routine ionospheric sounding at the ionosonde station at Slough in Berkshire, was celebrated on 11 January 1981. Over the years frequency scanned soundings had been carried out every hour of each day of the year. Data from the Slough ionosonde station and others was collated and distributed to various users who required long-term predictions of ionospheric conditions, or immediate forecasts of ionospheric disturbances of one kind or another. Others, such as the BBC, Marconi and Jodrell Bank, were supplied with noon critical frequency data each day.

Things have of course changed a little since those times. New technology has been introduced and the information data is now processed and disseminated by the Rutherford Appleton Laboratory located at Didcot in Oxfordshire. This is a world data centre, similar in function to that at Boulder, Colorado in the USA.

Figure 12   *Pulse ionosonde equipment designed by L. H. Bainbridge-Bell in 1933. Later ionosonde equipment was probably based on this. (Photo courtesy Rutherford Appleton Laboratory)*

The ionosonde

Ionosondes, or automatic ionospheric height sounders have been in use at various sites throughout the world for many years and were probably based on an earlier apparatus by L. H. Bainbridge-Bell, shown in Figure 12, and built in 1933 at the then Radio Research Station at Ditton Park, Slough.

A fully developed version of this, designed by R. Naismith and R. Bailey, was put into operation at Slough in 1945 and covered a total frequency range of 0.55 MHz to 17 MHz in five bands. Photographic readouts, known as 'ionograms' could be obtained in five minutes, or at the rate of 50 seconds per band. Various sequences could be used with regard to frequency range and a complete recording made automatically every 15 minutes. It could also be operated continuously for limited periods for solar and other eclipse observations and special events.

In 1948 it was decided to produce this equipment on a commercial basis for use in the UK and other countries. The basic specification was changed to include crystal control for the height, frequency markers and the timing sequences, and extend the frequency range to cover 0.6 to 25 MHz. The following is a general description of this ionosonde, although over the years numerous modifications have probably been made.

Later models cover a frequency range 0.55 to 23.8 MHz although the very low frequency section is rarely used because of interference to reception on the medium wave broadcast band. Some still produce a photographic record (or ionogram) showing the virtual height of the various ionospheric regions and critical frequency etc., as well as sporadic E events. The equipment is similar in external appearance to that by Naismith and Bailey which contained five main sections as follows:

1   Crystal controlled frequency divider unit
2   Linear calibrated timebase generator
3   Pulse modulated transmitter
4   Receiver, with its tuning locked to that of the transmitter via a servo system
5   Cathode ray tube display unit for direct observation and monitoring

With most ionosondes the transmitter peak pulse power is around 1 kilowatt but this can be changed slightly according to the frequency band in use. On routine recordings, ionospheric region heights are normally measured to the nearest 5 kilometres. The 'height' range readout starts at zero and continues to a maximum of 1200 kilometres (for recording multiples of echoes) although for special purposes this can be extended to 2000 kilometres. The pulse recurrence frequency is 50 per second and the pulse width variable from 80 to 300 microseconds.

A frequency readout accuracy to within 0.1 MHz is maintained, and with the use of an expanded time scale, height variations of the order of 1 kilometre can be measured.

Desirable characteristics for an ionosonde receiver, apart from accurate tuning in synchronism with the transmitter, is that the sensitivity must be inversely proportional to the power from the transmitter. This characteristic should include the transmitting and receiving aerials but is not a practical specification. Therefore a compromise is made to ensure that the sensitivity characteristic of each band covered by the receiver is reasonably flat so that the

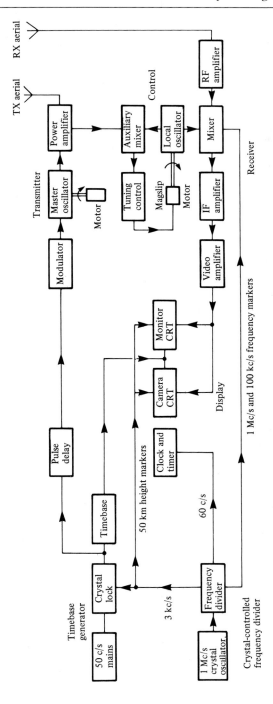

Figure 13   *Block diagram of an ionosonde transmitter/receiver by Naismith and Bailey (circa 1950–3). (Wireless Engineer)*

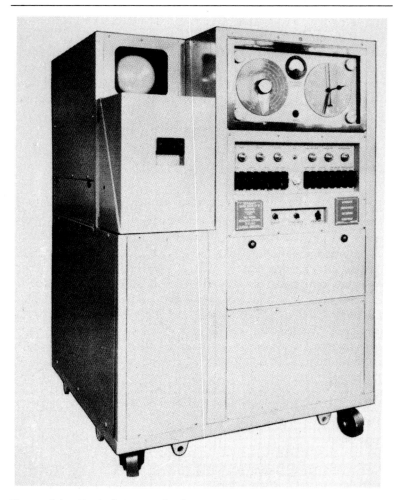

Figure 14 *Typical ionosonde frequency scanning transmitter/receiver. (Photo courtesy Rutherford Appleton Laboratory)*

gain of each band can be adjusted to compensate for the decrease in transmitter power with increasing frequency.

There must be no paralysis of the receiver input stages because of the direct and therefore very strong pulse signal from the transmitter. Pulse 'broadening' and delay of received signals (through the receiver) are reduced to a minimum consistent with the narrow bandwidth necessary to reject interfering signals. A block diagram of an ionosonde is shown in Figure 13. The height and frequency calibration circuitry is too complex to describe in detail but is nevertheless very accurate. It provides frequency markers along the photographic ionogram X axis and height markers along the Y axis. We can now deal with actual ionograms and the information they provide. A typical ionosonde is shown in Figure 14.

Ionograms

The examples shown in Figure 15 are typical of the earlier photographic records. This form of readout is being replaced by digital printout which is less costly.

The ionograms in Figure 15 have been chosen to show various ionospheric characteristics as described in the captions. First, however, some notes on 'height' calibration. This is provided by very narrow pulse markers at intervals related to the speed of radio waves in free space, i.e. 300×10 metres/second, or 186,000 miles/second. These markers are locked with the transmitted RF pulse and the timebase of a built-in CRT display. They also relate to the photographic or digital printouts.

It is easier to think in terms of 'milliseconds' as far as the time factor is concerned, and that a radio travels at 300 kilometres or 250 miles in 1 millisecond. If we assume an F region virtual height of 300 kilometres above earth, then a pulsed radio wave will take 1 millisecond to make the journey up to the region and the same time to return after reflection. Total distance travelled is 600 kilometres. Time taken is 2 milliseconds. The virtual height will be 'half' the total distance travelled, or 300 kilometres.

Figure 16, was taken from a dual trace CRT. It shows (trace A) the direct transmitted RF pulse and a series of 'echoes' from the F region in RF form as at the receiver intermediate frequency output stage. The second trace (B) shows the 'height' markers, the interval between each being 1 millisecond. The transmitted pulse is locked to the first marker and the first, or primary echo is just over the second marker indicating it has completed a journey to the F region and back in 2 milliseconds. Virtual height of region is therefore 300 kilometres. The secondary echoes are not directly height-related to the primary, thus indicating some anomaly at the time the photograph was taken.

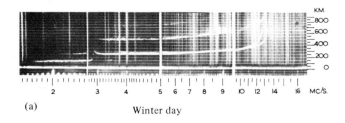

(a)   Winter day

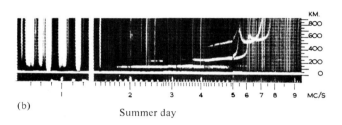

(b)   Summer day

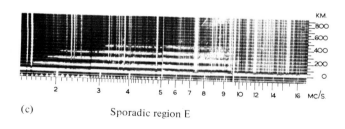

(c)   Sporadic region E

Figure 15   *Photographic readout ionograms. (a) A winter day ionogram of normal E and sporadic E from 1.6 to 2.8 MHz. The F region appears from 2.8 to 12.5 MHz with magnetoionic splitting near the critical frequency. The highest frequency reflected at vertical incidence is 12.5 MHz*

(b)   A quiet summer day ionogram showing normal E and sporadic E up to 4.8 MHz. Echoes from the F region appear from 3.7 to 7.6 MHz. Beyond 5 MHz magnetoionic splitting is apparent and the critical frequencies of the F1 and F2 regions are clearly shown

(c)   A good example of sporadic E return from 1.3 to about 9 MHz, the actual Es cloud height being 100 kilometres. Also to be seen are three multiples of the primary echo, each 100 km apart. (Ionograms courtesy Rutherford Appleton Laboratory)

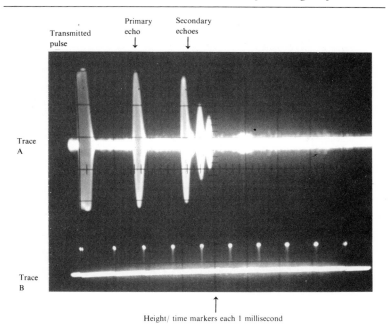

Figure 16 *Trace A F region echoes. Trace B 1 millisecond time markers (see text)*

Note that the received (direct) transmitter pulse and echoes are all subject to widening due to the number of tuned RF and IF amplifier stages in the receiver. The original width of the transmitted pulse (and of received echoes), as in Figure 16, is about 100 microseconds.

A further example of 'single frequency' ionospheric sounding is illustrated in Figure 17. Here we have not only the directly received transmitter pulse and a primary F region echo but also multi-reflected echoes. The upper trace (A) shows the rectified and amplified pulses derived from the RF pulses in the lower trace (B). In this case the primary echo is from a virtual height of about 300 kilometres, but note that the 'multiples' are equidistant, indicating that the original transmitted pulse has been reflected five times. That is, up to the region and down to earth, reflected from earth back up to the region and down again and so on. The last multiple, just visible, has travelled a total distance of $5 \times 600 = 3000$ kilometres. This rather indicates that a fairly intensely ionized F region and the earth can be quite efficient reflectors of radio waves.

33

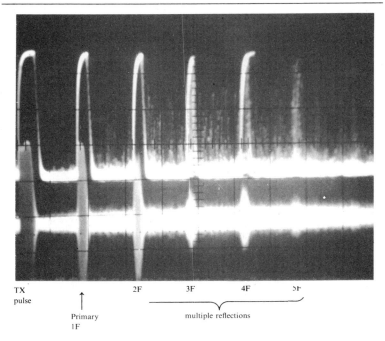

TX
pulse

2F   3F   4F   5F

Primary   multiple reflections
1F

Figure. 17   *Multiple reflections. F region primary echo at 300 kilometres.*
Multiples 1, 2, 3, 4 and 5F each separated by 100 kilometres (see text)

Multi-reflection from intense sporadic E can be even more dramatic as Figure 36 (Chapter 4) indicates.

Split echoes

The highest frequency that can be directly reflected from the F region is called the 'penetration frequency'. When this point is reached the original wave may be split into two characteristic waves by the earth's magnetic field. This produces two echoes, as shown in Figure 18(a) and (b), close to each other. In normal ionograms these are referred to as fo and fx respectively.

This 'split echo' effect, known as magnetoionic splitting, can be seen in yet another way from an ionogram produced by an ionosonde frequency scan. This is illustrated in Figure 19(a) in

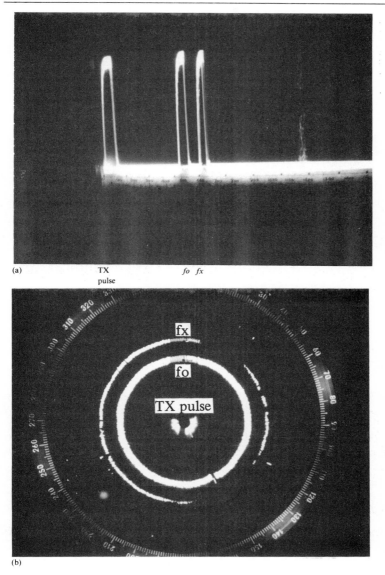

(a)   TX pulse   fo fx

(b)

Figure 18   *Magnetoionic splitting. (a) Shows split echo (F region)* fo *and* fx. *(b) The same as (a) but displayed by a rotating timebase. Duration of sweep 25 seconds. Centre: Transmitted pulse. First ring* fo *echo (continuous). Second ring* fx *echo which now shows discontinuity and splitting for intervals of a few seconds. Not always apparent in frequency sweep ionograms*

Ionosphere

Ionograms are radio soundings
giving reflection height (vertical scale)
versus radio frequency (horizontal scale)
from which are deduced properties of
the ionosphere

Ionosonde

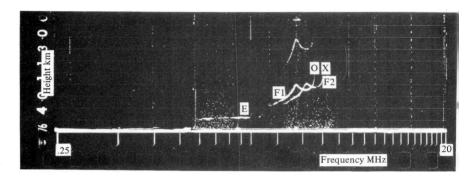

Daytime. Critical frequencies of normal E,
F1 and F2. 0 and X components of F layer
echoes clearly shown. Second order trace
illustrates higher absorption of X component

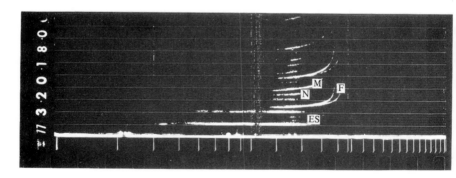

Night-time F layer blanketed to 2.9 MHz
by sporadic E (ES). Inter-layer reflections (M and N)

Figure 19 *(a) and (b) Typical ionograms but showing different aspects as
explained in text and annotations with photos. (Courtesy Rutherford
Appleton Laboratory)*

which the ordinary (fo) and extraordinary (fx) components (F region) can be seen at the end of the frequency sweep around 6 MHz. The lower ionogram (b) shows the result of inter-layer, M and N mode, reflections (see Chapter 4).

Effect of the earth's magnetic field

The earth's magnetic field and its effect on radio waves within an ionospheric region is a complex subject and does not warrant full explanation in this book since it is not vital as far as amateur radio is concerned. The following is therefore a brief outline. While the earth's magnetic field has no effect on radio waves travelling in the normal atmosphere, i.e. in ordinary air, in the ionosphere it can set 'free electrons' in motion. The behaviour of a radio wave is dependent on the character of this free electron motion because the 'paths' of the moving electrons are changed by the magnetic field. It remains that part of the wave is reflected from a point lower within the region, the ordinary component, while the other part of the wave, the extraordinary component, which has also been changed in frequency, appears as being reflected from a slightly greater height.

The frequency difference between the split waves depends on the 'strength' of the earth's magnetic field and which determines the magnitude of the free electron motion. The frequency difference between the fo and fx components varies in different parts of the earth but in mid-latitudes is about 0.6 MHz. The ordinary (critical) frequency is more important since it is used to determine MUFs.

General function of the ionospheric regions

Here we recap a little on the respective ionospheric regions which incidently include the 'Aurora Borealis' that occurs in the higher latitudes of the northern hemisphere, and the 'Aurora Australis' that occurs in the higher latitudes, below the equator, in the southern hemisphere. These are usually classified as ionospheric regions, because they do in fact become ionized by radiation from the sun and can reflect radio waves, notably those at VHF. (See Figure 32, Chapter 3.) Meteor trails can also become ionized and reflect radio waves.

The D region

This is the lowest region at a height of around 60 to 90 kilometres and is within a relatively dense part of the earth's atmosphere where atoms are broken up into ions by radiation from the sun but recombine fairly quickly at sunset. The D region will reflect waves at very low frequency but will also absorb energy from HF radio waves, often completely at frequencies around 3 to 4 MHz and often as high as 7 MHz. If the ionization is intense enough this region can prevent upward travelling HF waves from reaching the E or F regions and downcoming waves from either region from reaching earth, thus creating what is often called a 'radio blackout' which can last for periods of several minutes to several hours.

The E region

The lowest region that can provide long distance communication is the E region at a height above the surface of the earth of 100 to 120 kilometres (circa 65 miles). It is a region of fairly high atmospheric density and consequently, the ionization varies with the height of the sun above the horizon. Ultraviolet is not the only radiation from the sun that produces ionization in this region. A certain amount is caused by solar protons, X-rays and meteoric activity within the region. The ionization level drops rapidly at sunset when the ions and electrons recombine in the absence of sunlight. The E region reaches a minimum level of ionization after midnight, local time. It increases again rapidly at sunrise and reaches maximum around midday local time.

The E region can absorb energy from relatively low frequency waves during a period of maximum ionization.

Sporadic E (Es)

Fairly long-distance communication is often assisted by sporadic E which is due to the formation of densely ionized regions, generally called 'clouds' and thought to be produced by the action of 'shear winds' in the high atmosphere at a height of about 100 kilometres (60 miles). Es occurs mostly during the summer months, May, June, July and August but sometimes during the winter months (see Chapter 8–Data Section). If the ionization is intense enough, transmissions on the HF bands can be prevented from reaching the F region and/or being returned to earth. Sporadic E clouds drift at around 100 kilometres per hour although the 'area' of a cloud may vary considerably. If ionization is intense enough, transmissions in the 28 to 30 MHz band can be reflected or refracted and at much higher frequencies as well, e.g. at 145 MHz and higher. VHF contacts via sporadic E have been made over distances of 2000 miles or more.

The term 'sporadic E' (Es) is used because of the transient nature of the clouds.

The F region

Most long-distance communication on the HF bands is via the F region and when the critical frequency is high enough, the most used bands for DX are 14, 21 and 28 MHz. The virtual height of this region may vary depending on the time of the year, time of day, the latitude, and particularly the degree of sunspot activity. The mean virtual height of this region is 300 to 350 kilometres. It is during a period of maximum sunspot activity, which occurs around the peak of an eleven-year solar cycle, that consistently good world-wide DX conditions prevail for the 28 MHz band. It should be mentioned that the F region really consists of two regions, the F1 and F2, although for normal long distance propagation the F2 plays the major part.

The atmosphere at the height of these regions is very thin and the ions and electrons are slow to recombine. Because of this the level of ionization intensity is not so responsive to the height of the sun above the horizon. Ionization reaches maximum at, or a little after midday (local time) and falls to minimum just before sunrise. It then increases rapidly and can reach the daytime levels within a very few hours.

During the day the F region sometimes splits into the separate F1 and F2 regions with the lower and usually weaker F1 occurring at a virtual height of about 160 kilometres (nearly 100 miles). At night the F1 region disappears and the F2 region assumes a lower virtual height. (The anomalies of the F region are dealt with in Chapter 4 and other information will be found in Chapter 8.)

Skip distance

This a time-honoured term and more often than not used in an entirely wrong concept. However, what might be called the

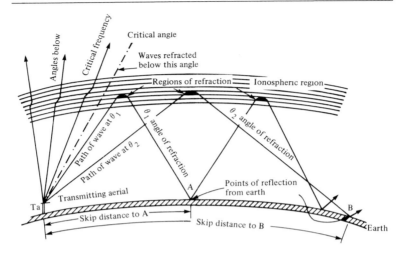

Figure 20   *The object of this illustration is to show (left) the 'angles' at which radio waves penetrate an ionospheric region at frequencies below critical frequency. Above critical frequency they are reflected (90 degrees incidence) or refracted at lower 'angles of incidence' for example θ_1 or θ_2, to be returned to earth at distances depending on those angles (see text)*

'standard' explanation, with illustration, becomes necessary to show how the term 'skip' applies to radio waves propagated via an ionospheric region.

If the ionization intensity of an ionospheric region is low and the frequency of transmission relatively high, i.e. above the critical frequency, a radio wave may be only very partially refracted and then continues on through the region to be lost in outer space. This occurs just before the 'critical angle' is reached as illustrated in Figure 20. Beyond this angle waves are refracted and returned to earth. The point at which a wave reaches earth after refraction depends on the angle at which it left the transmitting aerial in the first instance and which also determines the angle at which it leaves an ionospheric region.

This is also illustrated in Figure 20 first by the path of a wave from a transmitting aerial (Ta) at an angle θ_1 which, after refraction, reaches earth at point A and is then reflected back to the region. The ground distance between Ta and point A, is usually described as the 'skip distance' in this case 'short skip' as the distance is relatively short.

In the case of the path from Ta at angle θ_2 the wave will reach earth at a greater (skip) distance at point B. This path continues back to the region after the wave is reflected from earth. Since θ_2 is lower the ground distance (Ta to B) is much greater and usually referred to as 'long skip'. A more realistic explanation is given in Chapter 6.

Ionospheric region height and transmission distance

The greatest distance that can be covered in one 'hop' by virtue of very low vertical angle radiation from the transmitting aerial, is approximately 4000 kilometres (2500 miles) when wave propagation is via the F region. The maximum distance covered with propagation from the E region and again with very low vertical angle radiation from the aerial, is about 2000 kilometres or 1250 miles. These distances are based on virtual heights of around 300 to 350 kilometres for the F region and about 100 kilometres for the E region. To achieve either, the vertical angle of maximum radiation must in fact be zero, or tangential to the surface of the earth. If the whole transmission distance is to exceed that obtained by the first hop then additional hops must follow.

Taking an F region height as above, and an 'average' vertical angle of maximum radiation between 20 and 30 degrees for one of the higher frequency bands, e.g. 21 or 28 MHz, the approximate distance covered by a single hop would be in the region of 1600 to 2400 kilometres (1000 to 1500 miles). See Chapter 8.

Low vertical angle radiation is important when operating on the higher frequency bands. On the other hand, high angle radiation, more often than not the case with aerials for the 160, 80 and 40 metre bands, can be an added bonus as we shall see later. Propagation over long distances on these bands is usually by a series of short hops.

Virtual height and critical frequency

Ionospheric region 'virtual height' is not the height to the base, or lower boundary of the region, but to a point where the ionization intensity is great enough to reflect a radio wave transmitted from earth at an angle of 90 degrees. The critical frequency also varies with the ionization intensity and becomes higher as the ionization increases. Ionization intensity is usually greatest during the peak period of a solar sunspot cycle for both the E and F regions, although there are variations for summer and winter time. Critical frequencies are lowest during the minimum period of the solar sunspot cycle and again with variations during summer and winter time. (See Chapter 3 for further information.)

Maximum usable frequency

With long-distance radio communication via ionospheric propagation, it is desirable to know what is called the maximum usable frequency (MUF). As already mentioned this can be derived from knowing the critical frequency of the ionospheric region concerned and taking into account local time, summer or winter time, and the prevailing eleven-year solar cycle conditions. For DX conditions on the HF amateur bands and with propagation via the F region, the MUF will be about 3.5 times the critical frequency, allowing also for the time of day, season of the year, and the solar cycle period as above. Ideally, the frequency of operation should be just below the MUF. (Data available for determining MUF from prevailing critical frequency, including first hop distance for given vertical angle of maximum radiation is given in Chapter 8.)

Lowest usable frequency

If an amateur band frequency is below the MUF at any particular time, the signal strength at the point of reception may be reduced because of greater absorption within the ionospheric region. If the operational frequency is lower still, the received signals may disappear altogether. There is however a lower limit in terms of frequency which, with certain ionospheric conditions, allows propagation for limited distances. The frequency is called the lowest usable frequency (LUF) although distance etc. depends on the transmitter power used and the directivity gain of the aerial system. It is good practice, whenever possible, to operate on a frequency about 15 per cent below the MUF, assuming this is within an allocated amateur band. This lower frequency is sometimes called the optimum working frequency (OWF), although the French, frequence optimum de travail (FOT), is sometimes used.

It is appreciated that it may not always be possible to transmit on a particular MUF or OWF with fixed frequency bands. As already intimated, the critical frequency, time of day, season of the year, and prevailing period of the solar cycle must be taken into account in order to ascertain the best usable frequency band.

Otherwise the chances of working worthwhile DX on any band, at any particular time, may well depend on either experience at estimating band conditions by listening round, or being fortunate enough to have just the right ionospheric conditions at the time. It must be said that experienced DX operators will soon be on when 'conditions' are good or, as some say, the band has opened up.

References

1 'Radio and Space Research at Slough 1920–1981', *The Radio and Electronics Engineer*, Gardiner, Lane and Risbeth, Vol. 52, No. 3, March 1982.
2 'Automatic Ionospheric Height Recorder', *Wireless Engineer*, Clarke and Shearman, Sept. 1953.
3 'Sun, Earth and Radio', *Radio Sounding of the Upper Atmosphere*, J. A. Ratcliffe (World University Library 1970).
4 *Radio Waves and the Ionosphere*, T. W. Bennington (Iliffe & Sons 1944).

3 The eleven-year solar cycles and sunspot activity

During the last fifty years, sunspot counts have become important data used in connection with ionospheric radio wave propagation. So also have the eleven-year solar cycles during which the sunspot counts rise and fall (between the start and finish of each cycle) resulting in variation in the different kinds of radiation from the sun, some of which reach earth for example, natural light, infra-red and ultra violet. The real connection between ionospheric radio wave propagation and radiation from the sun is the ionization of the different regions.

This has been mentioned briefly in the previous chapters but before going a little deeper into this aspect, some historical facts and figures concerned with solar cycles and sunspots may prove to be of interest.

Many may be surprised to discover that records of solar cycle observations date back to about 650 BC. Although these records are not particularly accurate they do show the eleven-year trend. Later records exist, from about AD 300, and while not completely reliable, do provide data that is a little more accurate. It should be kept in mind however, that all the solar cycles ever recorded cover only a minute span in the life of the sun and that of the earth itself. While science can provide reasonable proof of the latter (acceptable or not) the real concern here is that the solar cycles do occur, the sunspots (including other surface phenomena) appear, albeit irregularly and HF radio wave propagation is effected accordingly.

While the sun has been around a long time there is no record of the existence of the ionospheric regions before the time of their discovery, some eighty years ago, or that they will continue to exist. The fact that the sun has behaved in a more or less regular fashion, as far as the solar cycles are concerned, is not necessarily proof that this phenomenon will continue indefinitely either. No

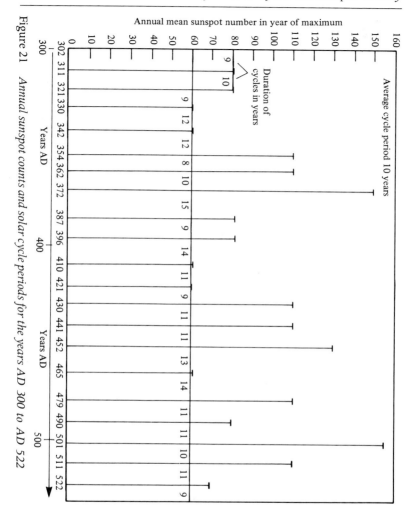

Figure 21 *Annual sunspot counts and solar cycle periods for the years AD 300 to AD 522*

doubt both will serve us well for a long time yet, of that we can be reasonably sure. However, solar cycles may not be related only to ionospheric radio propagation. Long before even Marconi was born, it was thought that the cycles affected the earth's weather in some way as will be illustrated later.

It should also be noted that the solar cycles are not always of eleven years duration. Some have lasted for fifteen years and some for only eight years, as shown by a very early record covering the period AD 300 to just beyond AD 530 (Figure 21).

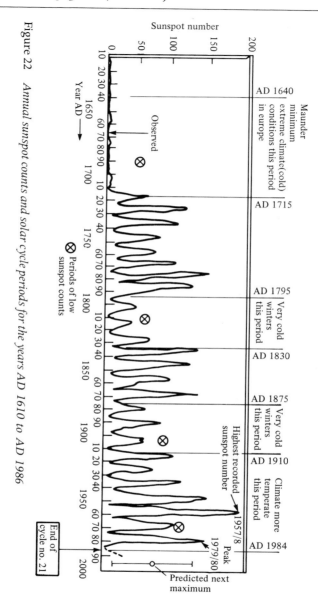

Figure 22 *Annual sunspot counts and solar cycle periods for the years AD 1610 to AD 1986*

Had we been around with HF band transmitting and receiving equipment during the years 1650 to 1715, not very much DX would have been worked. This was known as the 'Maunder minimum' which coincided with a period of extreme climatic conditions over the whole of Europe. For example, in 1683 and 1684 fairs, or should it be fayres?, were held in London on the frozen river Thames. The Maunder minimum also shows up in carbon-14 analyses of tree rings, the carbon-14 content indicating cosmic ray intensity at the time the wood was formed. Because the cosmic ray flux on earth is modulated by solar activity, it is now thought that carbon-14 analyses also indicated solar activity. Such analyses, covering a period of around 7000 years, show recurring fluctuations that suggest times of either high, or low, solar activity.

As can be seen in Figure 22, the Maunder minimum lasted about 100 years, during which solar activity was virtually non-existent, hence the previous comment that little DX would have worked during that period! During the later part of this event there is some semblance of eleven-year cycles (1650 to 1710) after which the cycles assume greater amplitudes. By about 1795, and more or less a hundred years later, another period of low solar activity occurred and this also coincided with exceptionally cold winters which prevailed for some thirty-five years. Between 1875 and 1910 there was another similar period of low solar activity and very cold winter weather, after which solar cycle peaks gradually increased in amplitude until the present time. Sunspot counts became higher reaching an all-time level at the peak of cycle no. 20 with a count of almost 200. Needless to say this was a good time for DX on the higher frequency bands, as also during the peak of 1979–80 (highest sunspot count 150).

At the time of writing, early 1986, the solar cycle no. 21 is approaching its minimum, and conditions for DX on the higher bands 14, 21, 28 MHz are poor. The minimum of this cycle just appears in Figure 22 but more of this later.

The active sun and sunspots

Most radio amateurs and short-wave listeners are familiar with sunspots and indeed many make a study of them, or at least carry out observations, when the sun is clearly visible, to see how many individual spots or groups of spots can be seen. This is quite easy

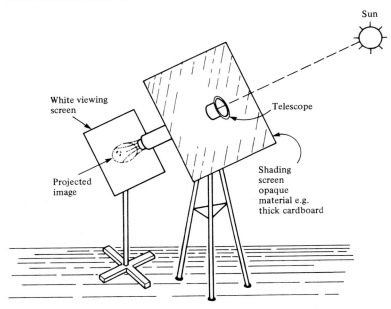

Figure 23   *Method of using a telescope to project an image of the sun on to a white screen for sunspot observation. Warning – never look at the sun directly through a telescope even with a dark filter fitted. This could cause severe eye damage or even blindness*

to do with the aid of a reasonably good telescope, using this to focus a fairly large and clear 'picture' of the sun on to a white screen as shown in Figure 23.

WARNING Never look at the sun directly through a telescope or binoculars, not even with a dark filter fitted. Direct magnified sunlight can cause severe damage to the eyes and even blindness.

One of the most notable phenomena on the surface of the sun is the appearance and disappearance of dark areas known as 'sunspots'. The life of these spots is variable, some last only a few days, whilst others may survive during four or five solar rotations, each of which take about twenty-seven days. The exact nature of sunspots is not known but they appear to be vortices in the matter known as the 'photosphere'. Sunspots appear dark because their surface temperature is only about 3000 degrees K, compared with that of the quiet photosphere at 6000 degrees K.

Sunspots tend to group together and a single group may consist of a few isolated spots, or a relatively large number. One of the interesting features of sunspots is their unusually strong magnetic fields which may approach 0.4 Wb/m (weber per square metre = 4000 G) for the larger spots.

To show more clearly the variations in solar sunspot activity the full readout of sunspot counts for the whole of solar cycle no. 21 is given as Figure 24. However, to measure this activity an index is required, the most common being the Wolf number R given by

$$R = k(10g + s)$$

where g is the number of groups and s is the number of observable individual spots. The term k is a correction factor to take into account variations in equipment and observer characteristics. The fact that this number is weighted in favour of groups, makes its value as an index of sunspot activity somewhat questionable. Nevertheless, the data it offers is usable, and has been for about 200 years. In addition to the relatively dark sunspots, bright areas often appear on the solar surface and are known as 'plages'. They are closely associated with sunspots, often preceding them and persisting after the sunspots, which develop in them, have disappeared.

Solar flares

A solar flare is rather like a burst of light and occurs in the chromosphere near a sunspot. They are most easily observed in Hα light (6563 A) but there are rare cases when flares have been visible in 'white light'. As solar observations are virtually continuous most of the flares that occur on the solar hemisphere facing the earth can be seen. They occur quite frequently, particularly during the peak period of a solar cycle.

Solar flares are rated in terms of importance, for example $1 -$, $1 +$, 2, $2 +$, 3 and $3 +$ etc. according to brightness and area. Also the duration of a flare increases with its importance e.g., a 1 flare may last about 20 minutes and a 3 flare about 60 minutes. The life of a flare may also vary somewhat from the mean value. Very small flares, smaller than '1', are referred to as sub-flares.

A solar flare develops very rapidly to peak intensity, which is brief, followed by a steady decline. There is also a 'statistical'

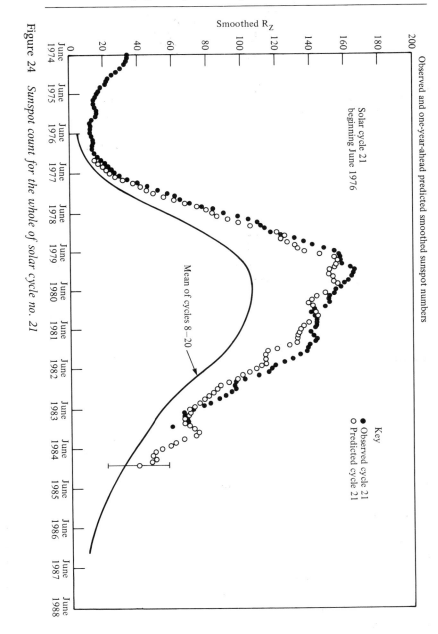

Figure 24   *Sunspot count for the whole of solar cycle no. 21*

relation between the number of flares that occur during one solar rotation (Nf) and the corresponding mean sunspot numbers (R). With the occurrence of some flares there is often a noticeable increase in the flux of solar ionizing radiation in the far ultra-violet and soft X-ray region of the spectrum (see Figure 25) which affects the electron densities in the D and E regions.

Solar radio emissions

The sun radiates thermal radio emissions all the time, although the level of these emissions greatly increases during solar flares and when active regions become visible. During a solar flare, radio emission is complex in both time and spectrum, a subject beyond the scope of present knowledge. However, total emission from the sun, at radio wavelengths, is in fact a useful indicator of solar activity and in particular at a wavelength of approximately 10 cm (10.7 cm is commonly used) and the quantity is known as the 10.7 cm solar flux. One advantage of the radio method is that information can still be obtained even when the sun is not visible because of cloud banks. An example of comparison between sunspot count, 10.7 cm solar flux, and critical frequency, covering thirty days during September 1984 is given in Figure 26.

Sunspot numbers

In addition to what has already been said about sunspots, the following notes made available by the National Geophysical Data Centre, Boulder, Colorado, USA, may be of interest. In 1848 the Swiss astronomer, Johann Rudolph Wolf, introduced a daily measurement of sunspot numbers and his method, which is still used today, counts the total number of spots visible on the face of the sun, and the number of groups into which they cluster. Neither quantity alone satisfactorily measures sunspot activity.

So, an observer computes a daily sunspot number by multiplying the number of groups he sees by ten and then adding this product to his total count of individual spots. Results however, vary greatly, since the measurement strongly depends on observer interpretation and experience and on the stability of the earth's atmosphere above the observing site. Moreover, the use of the earth as a platform from which to record these numbers,

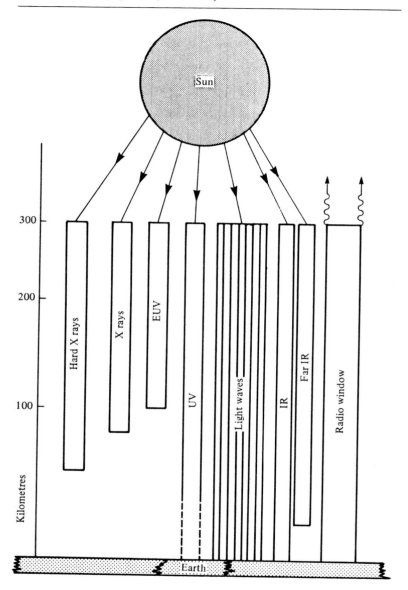

Figure 25 *Radiation from the sun. (Courtesy of USA Airforce, Cambridge Laboratories, Maine, USA)*

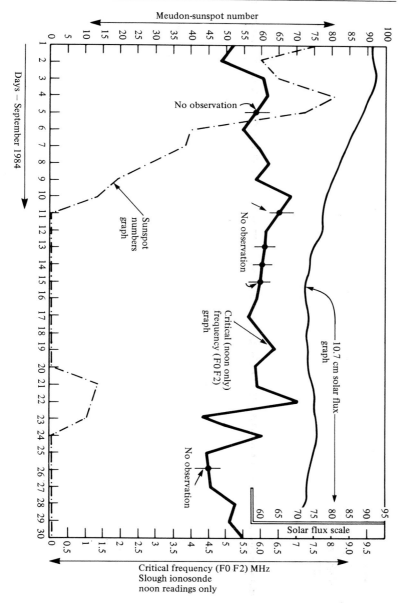

Figure 26 *Critical frequencies related to sunspot counts and 10.7 centimetre solar flux over a period of 30 days, September 1984*

contributes to variability because the sun rotates and the evolving spot groups are distributed unevenly across solar longitudes. To compensate for these limitations, each daily international number is computed as a weighted average of measurements made from a network of cooperating observatories.

The end of sunspot cycle no. 21

This cycle began its rise from minimum, at the end of the previous cycle 20, in about June 1976 (the full cycle is shown in Figure 24) and it is interesting to follow its progress downward from the peak which occurred in about December 1979 with an R (sunspot) count of about 165. The time from the beginning of the cycle to its peak is about three and a half years. However, the cycle plot ends at October 1984, or about five years from the time of the peak, making the total years to that time about eight and a half. This is *not* likely to be a short cycle as data will eventually show. So, taking the full eleven years, the end of cycle no. 21 would occur about the end of 1987.

At the time of writing, cycle 21 has not yet reached its minimum, although there are signs that this is not far off as daily observations have shown. Prediction of the time of the end of this cycle will be dealt with in due course.

Changing conditions during eleven-year cycles

The conditions produced during the period over which a solar cycle is falling toward its minimum can be illustrated and to this it is necessary to go back to cycle no. 20, as at January 1973, or about three and a half years before the minimum of that cycle and the start of cycle no. 21. Figure 27(a) illustrates the noon (GMT) Fo–F2 critical frequency variation, for January 1973, and as can be seen, the frequencies are fairly high, most of the time being above 7 MHz, with the highest on day 5 at 9.2 MHz. This condition signified favourable DX on the HF bands, up to and including the 28 MHz band.

Figure 27(b) is for May 1976, one month prior to the minimum of that cycle (20) when the noon (GMT) Fo–F2 critical frequencies averaged at only around 5 MHz, the highest being, on day 17, at 6 MHz. This resulted in generally poor DX conditions but some

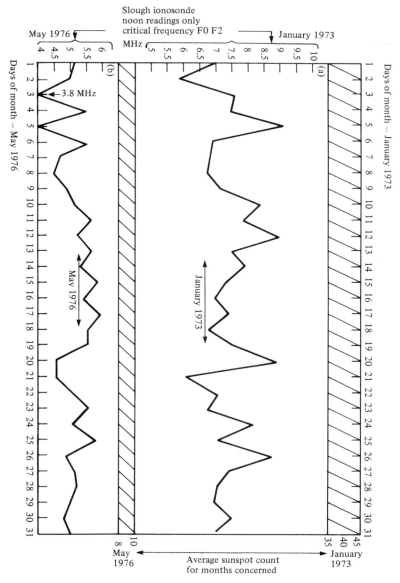

Figure 27   *Critical frequencies v sunspot counts (a) January 1973 and (b) May 1976*

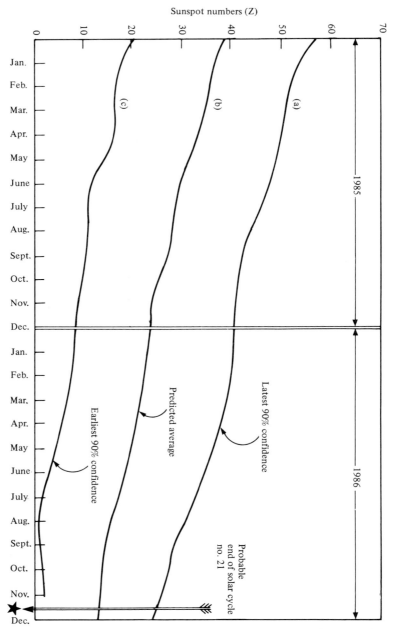

Figure 28 *McNish-Lincoln predictions for end of solar cycle no. 21 (see text for explanation)*

activity on 14 MHz according to the time of day.

Now a similar case but this time for September 1984 during the 'falling' period of cycle no. 21. Information supplied by the Rutherford Appleton Laboratory, World Data Centre, indicates a gradual though erratic fall in the noon Fo–F2 critical frequencies, the highest being 7.1 MHz on day 22; coincident with a small rise in sunspot activity, during days 21 to 23 as illustrated in Figure 26. The fall in the 10.7 cm solar flux is consistent with the fall in the Fo–F2 noon critical frequencies and the sunspot count. At this time DX was already poor, with little or no activity on the 21 and 28 MHz amateur bands.

Prediction of the end of solar cycle no. 21 and the beginning of cycle no. 22

From information contained in the *Sunspot Data Bulletin No. 7*, Royal Belgian Observatory, Brussels, the graphs in Figure 28 have been produced using the McNish-Lincoln prediction method. These curves show the continuation of the fall toward minimum with a 90 per cent confidence *latest* and *earliest* as well as a predicted average. The earliest possible time for the solar minimum, as in Figure 28 curve (c), is August/September 1986, because the 90 per cent earliest has reached bottom and started to rise. The *predicted average* curve (b) indicates that the solar minimum will occur later than December 1986 because it is still falling, although gradually. Probability on this is April/May 1987. The third curve (a), also still falling and fairly rapidly at that, puts the minimum much later, probably October/November 1987.

Further analysis of prediction with a computer is shown by the two readouts, Figures 29 and 30. The indication is that the minimum of solar cycle no. 21 will occur about December 1986 after which DX conditions will improve, slowly at first, but becoming more consistent as solar cycle no. 22 goes toward its maximum.

DX predictions

Based on data supplied from various sources, some magazines devoted to amateur radio publish DX predictions for the month

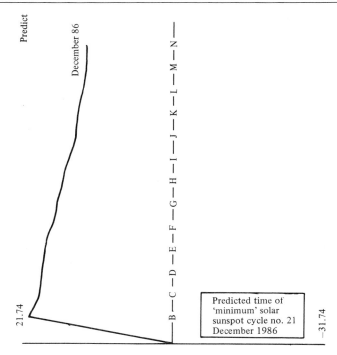

Figure 29 *Computer analysis. Predicted end of solar cycle no. 21 (see also Figure 30)*

for the different HF bands. Although these predictions provide some guidance they are not infallible.

With certain information to hand, it is possible to obtain a close approximation as to what distances can and cannot be worked at almost any time of the day or night. Again the method is not infallible. This is because the changing ionospheric conditions and anomalies that can occur over long paths (day and night, or both) cannot themselves be predicted. At the end of this book will be found computerized data that applies to the above.

The solar cycle and critical frequency

The frequency at which there is no reflection from the F region and when the angle of incidence of a radio wave is 90 degrees to the plane of the region, is known as the 'critical frequency'.

Information

Predict

Column		Value*	Percentage
B	Dec. 84	31.74	9.86
C	Jan.	29.83	9.27
D	Feb.	29.02	9.02
E	Mar.	28.30	8.79
F	Apr.	27.28	8.48
G	May	25.86	8.03
H	June	24.52	7.62
I	July	23.28	7.23
J	Aug.	21.82	6.78
K	Sept.	20.94	6.50
L	Oct.	20.28	6.30
M	Nov.	19.45	6.04
N	Dec.	19.36	6.01

Note: B is reference only. Computed sunspot count Dec. 1984

Months relate to both 1985 and 1986

* Computed sunspot counts. Combined years 1985 and 1986, Jan. to Dec. Last figure (19.36) rounded to 19 or 20 as approximation of sunspot count during period of turn round from end of cycle 21 to beginning of cycle 22.

100% = 321.68

Figure 30 *Computer information relating to Figure 29. Percentage sunspot counts (6.1%) = point where the cycle should bottom with a Zs count of 19.36*

As already mentioned in a previous chapter, this varies with the intensity of ionization which is dependent on the amount of radiation from the sun. There is, however, some consistency as far as the critical frequency is concerned in relation to the time of day or night, the season of the year, i.e. winter or summer, and the period of the solar cycle minimum or maximum. The maximum usable frequency is related to the critical frequency by a factor of about 3.5.

The critical frequency (fo–F2) curves shown in Figure 31 show mean values for the various conditions as in the previous paragraph. They cover a 24-hour period for the seasons and solar cycle minimum and/or maximum periods. By selecting the crit: fo for time, season and solar period, and multiplying this by 3.5, one can get a reasonable approximation of the prevailing MUF. For example, the time of day is 1100 hours GMT, the season winter, the solar cycle at maximum. The crit: fo is 12 MHz so the MUF will be in the region of $12 \times 3.5 = 42$ MHz. A condition that would

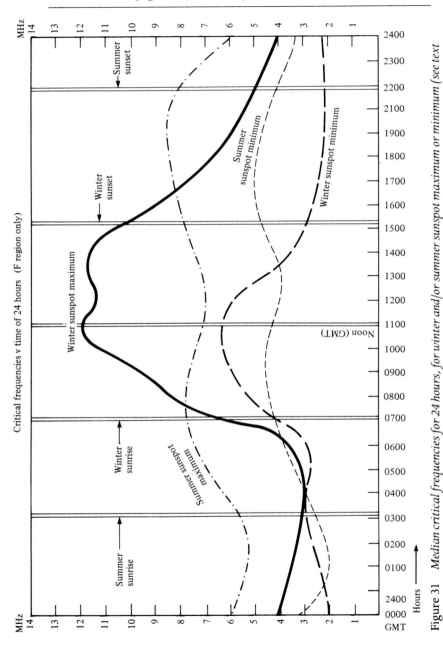

Critical frequencies v time of 24 hours (F region only)

Figure 31 *Median critical frequencies for 24 hours, for winter and/or summer sunspot maximum or minimum (see text for examples of how to ascertain MUF)*

ensure some excellent DX right up to the 28–30 MHz region and which would be nice to have every day, year in and year out.

By way of contrast, the F2 crit: fo for 1500 hours GMT for summer period and solar minimum, would be about 4.2 MHz so the MUF would be in the region of 14.7 MHz. Amateur radio bands up to 14 MHz should be active.

Note: The critical frequency curves in Figure 31 apply only to the UK as they are based on noon (GMT) observations. They could accordingly be used at other longitudes in the northern hemisphere at latitudes around 50 degrees, providing the midday (noon) and the 24-hour time is taken as 'local' time and with the seasons selected accordingly. If applied to southern hemisphere latitudes, also around 50 degrees, it must also be remembered that the climatic seasons are reversed. Again depending on longitude, the noon point and 24-hour times will have to be related to 'local' time.

Ionospheric region variations

Radio communication on the HF bands over long distances relies solely on ionospheric wave propagation but there are variations over which we have no control. If such variations are ignored and operating frequencies are chosen randomly, the possibilities of DX contacts and indeed communication closer to home, will be equally random. For example, signals may well be lost into outer space because they have penetrated the ionosphere, or because of absorption in the lower D region, on the way up, or on the way down, i.e. from a distant transmitter and so on. It is worth paying at least some attention to choosing the right time of day (or night), the right frequency band having regard to MUF and critical frequency, and the solar cycle period. In this respect some easy-to-use data is included later. Last but not least the aerial also plays a very important part whether used for transmitting and receiving, or receiving only.

Ionized reflecting media

As a form of summary to this chapter it seems worthwhile to recap on the reflecting (or refracting) regions. To this end the illustration Figure 32 has been prepared. It provides the respective

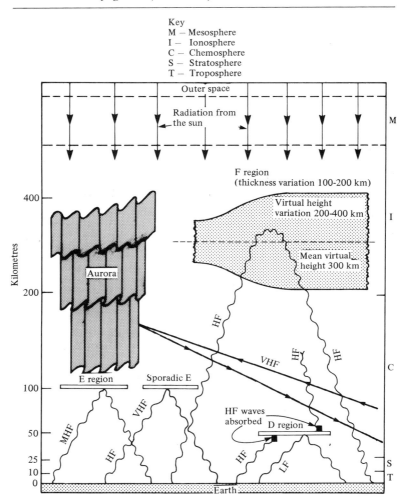

Figure 32   *Respective heights and other data concerned with ionospheric regions including Aurora, but which is effective mostly at VHF. (Courtesy of USA Airforce, Cambridge Laboratories, Maine, USA)*

virtual heights of the ionospheric regions, including the aurorae which normally play no part in HF propagation except during severe magnetic storms. An auroral curtain may then move toward the equator and give rise to complex reflections which can effect transmissions at quite low frequencies (3 to 5 MHz). The aurorae do however reflect laterally at VHF, as many 2-metre operators will confirm.

Apart from causing 'radio blackouts', because of dense ionization, the D region does propagate very long wavelength transmissions and has a mean height of about 60 to 90 kilometres. The E region is concerned mainly with the propagation of medium wave transmissions at night and like the D region, is averagely only a few kilometres in thickness.

On the other hand the formation of sporadic E 'clouds' at the same height as the E region, i.e. about 100 kilometres, will propagate both HF and VHF waves but such clouds are, as the name implies, 'sporadic' (occurring at irregular points in time – intermittent – isolated and moving). Finally the F region (normally the amalgamation of F1 and F2 regions) has a mean virtual height of 300 to 350 kilometres and a thickness that varies between about 100 and 200 kilometres depending on the time of day. *Propagation*: HF radio waves in the range about 3 to 30 MHz, or higher, depending on the degree of ionization.

The origin of the sunspot numbers

Rudolf Wolf introduced the so-called sunspot numbers as a measure of sunspot activity in the year 1848. They are based on the fact that sunspots most frequently appear in groups. Observations, carried out daily, required that the total number (f) of the visible spots, regardless of size, were counted. Secondly, the number of groups (g) were also counted. Wolf found that a large group could contain as many as 100 individual spots whereas smaller groups contained just a few, or even only a single spot. It follows that although f may usually be greater than g it can on the other hand be equal to g in cases where a group consists of a single spot. By itself the g number does not provide a satisfactory measure of activity because the sizes of the groups differ. The number f is not valid either, as an increase in activity is created when a new spot appears in a region where there were none. Much the same applies when a new spot appears in an existing group (see Figure 33). Wolf therefore introduced the expression ($10 \times g + f$) which, although considered somewhat arbitary, has proved successful over the years.

The g and f numbers do of course depend on the power of the instrument used for observation. The observation carried out by Wolf were with a Fraunhofer refractor having an aperture of 8 cm, a focal length of 110 cm, and a magnification of 64. This refractor,

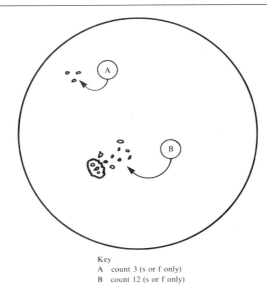

Key
A   count 3 (s or f only)
B   count 12 (s or f only)

Figure 33   *Sunspots. Small group of single spots and group of spots with penumbra*

provided with a polarizing helioscope, was still in use around 1960. Wolf indicated that he would have liked to measure the 'areas' covered by sunspots in order to determine the numbers, but with the limitations of the equipment at that time he was unable to produce drawings to scale from the projected image. photographic techniques had not been developed sufficiently, and while 'area' measurements were carried out they showed that over periods of years the sunspot relative numbers were more or less proportional.

The definition that Wolf had already established continued to be used. It was very evident however, that on any one day the sunspot number and the spot area could deviate quite considerably. A single large spot with penumbra had little influence as far as the number was concerned and covered a sizeable area, but a group consisting of a large number of small spots could occupy a small area and yield a high sunspot number.

In order to cater for the gaps in observations (when the sun was obscured by cloud) which in turn led to rather erratic results, Wolf decided he needed 'collaborators' located at places as far distant as possible from each other and himself. The idea was that they should also make daily observations and record the results using the f and g format. So more than a hundred years ago sunspot observation became international and has remained so to the present time.

Around 1960 some thirty professional observatories and about the same number of 'amateur' observers were contributing. By 1957 a special station known as the Specola Solare at Locarno-Monti in Italy had been built on the southern side of the Alps, where the weather conditions were complimentary to those in Zurich located on the northern side. The combined observations from Zurich, Locarno, and another specially built observatory at Arosa in Switzerland, revealed few gaps. Nevertheless, the first sunspot number 'readouts' were sent out each month to more than a hundred institutes and broadcast by the Swiss short-wave service every month.

It was found however, that some observers obtained different counts largely due to variations in the instruments used and also the personal 'counting method', so anomalies still occurred. To off-set this a 'personal' factor k was introduced and from which the Zurich sunspot count was derived. The formula became,

$$R = k \, (10 \times g + f), \text{ or } R = k \, (10g + s)$$

Originally a k factor of 1 was used but this was later changed to 0.06 to account for shortcomings in observatory equipment and personal interpretation.

Individual sunspots and groups of sunspots may persist for several months and therefore reappear during successive solar rotations. Sunspot numbers as observed, show a strong 27-day periodicity and for many purposes are 'smoothed' to highlight changes over longer periods. This is done by taking daily averages over a month, or monthly averages over a year. Hence the term 'smoothed sunspot count', or Zurich smoothed count (Zs).

Sunspot count information

The Radio Society of Great Britain transmit news bulletins every Sunday which, apart from specific information for members of the Society, include items concerned with radio wave propagation and also sunspot counts for the week. These transmissions go out on the 3.5 MHz HF band. Frequency 3.65 MHz, or nearest, depending on occupation by other stations. Time (GMT) 0900 hours and then every half hour up to 1100 hours.

The same news bulletins are transmitted on VHF, also on Sundays at various times and frequencies for different parts of the UK (145 MHz–2-metre band).

Further details are available from The Radio Society of Great Britain, Lambda House, Cranbourne Road, Potters Bar, Herts EN6 3JW.

The Swiss Broadcasting Corporation also transmit weekly sunspot counts. The address is SBC, Swiss Broadcasting Corporation, Giacomettistraase 3, CH 3000 Bern 15, Switzerland.

References

1 *Climate. Past, Present and Future*, Prof. H. H. Lamb (2 volumes) (Methuen, Barnes Noble).
2 *The Upper Atmosphere and Solar Terrestrial Relations*, J. K. Hargreaves (Van Nostrand Reinhold).
3 'Radio Communication and Sunspots', *Practical Wireless*, J. Kenewell, April 1983.
4 *Ionospheric Radio Propagation*, K. Davies (Dover Publications).
5 Sunspot Bulletin No. 7, Ed Resp, Dr Andre Koeckelenburgh, Ave. Circulaire 3, B-1180, Bruxelles, Belgium.
6 *Solar News*, The London Solar Committee, Issue 11, Oct. 1985.
7 'The 11-Year Sunspot Cycles', *Practical Wireless*, F. C. Judd, March/April 1986.
8 *Solar Indices Bulletin*, Aug. 1984, National Geophysical Centre, 325 Broadway, Boulder, Colorado, USA.
9 *Sunspot Activity in the Years 1610–1960*, Prof. M. Waldmeier (Zurich Sculthess & Co. AG. 1961).

4 Ionospheric anomalies

The ionospheric regions do not behave in a perfectly constant manner and there are a number of different ways in which anomalies (deviation from the normal, i.e. irregularity or inconsistency) can affect HF radio signals propagated via the ionosphere. Moreover, the state of the ionospheric regions can vary considerably over long paths and change by day and night. The latter means that 'conditions', as most radio amateurs call them, will be different in the illuminated half of the earth from those in the darkened part. There will also be differences between the northern and southern hemispheres, and yet frequently radio amateurs operating on the HF bands, as well as the short-wave broadcast stations, can frequently communicate between the light and dark zones and/or the two hemispheres of the earth. In fact it is not uncommon for a listening station in the UK to hear 'round-the-world echoes' from a station transmitting in the UK. The listening station will hear both the direct and indirect signals that have travelled around the world and back. This effect is easily recognizable by the 'time delay' which, depending on the total distance, is some fraction of a second. This event is mostly heard during a solar maximum period when good ionospheric conditions prevail, particularly for the higher frequency bands, e.g. 21 and 28 MHz.

The anomalies that can occur are numerous, and during normal operating conditions one may never know exactly what they are, the only indication being that 'conditions' have suddenly changed for some unexplainable reason. For example, the station you were in contact with announces that your signals, previously S9, have virtually disappeared, and yet his signals are still coming in at good strength or vice versa.

Trans-equatorial openings

Propagation between the northern and southern hemispheres (or vice versa) was mentioned in the previous paragraph. There is a period of a year or so during the eleven-year solar cycle minimum when the F region MUF does not reach 28 MHz in temperate latitudes, and which mainly affects east-to-west propagation. Trans-equatorial propagation (north/south path) is frequently possible, even when the sunspot count is less than five, although such a low figure is rarely reached. There is also a small but fairly regular variation in sunspot activity over a period of around 28 days, the time taken for the sun to make a single axial rotation. This can result in a rise and fall in MUF, causing changes in propagation conditions from about 14 up to 28 MHz.

Polarization and direction of travel

Because of the nature of refraction in the ionospheric regions, the polarization of a refracted wave is more often than not changed from what it was at the place of transmission. It is not necessary to use aerials with the same polarization. Whilst most radio amateurs use horizontally polarized aerials, especially for the lower frequency bands, many employ vertically polarized aerials, more so for the higher frequency bands when it is often more convenient to use a 'multi-band' vertical. However, depending on the type of aerial, the polarization of the radiated wave may tend to be elliptical.

Generally speaking a radio wave that travels a very long distance follows the most direct path between the places of transmission and reception, i.e. a great circle path. However, because of ionospheric variations the real path may deviate by as much as 5 degrees from the true great circle path.

Great circle paths

There are always two great circle paths between any two points on the earth's surface. One is the shortest distance between them, the other being a path in exactly the opposite direction but not necessarily longer, i.e. the two paths could be equidistant. Most of the time radio communication takes place over the shorter path.

Long path propagation is not uncommon however, and at certain times of the day (or night) when the short path cannot be used because of ionospheric conditions, it is often possible to establish contact via a long path. This is one reason for having a rotating beam aerial. Long path contacts in excess of 30,000 kilometres (nearly 20,000 miles) are not unusual, particularly at sunrise and sunset, local time.

Spurious directivity

Quite often radio waves appear to arrive from directions that have no apparent relationship to the actual direction from which a transmission originated (detectable with a beam aerial). This may be due to the behaviour of the ionospheric region concerned, often the F region and a common cause is 'scattering', an effect to be dealt with later. False directivity could also be due to spurious responses from the aerial itself giving the impression that the 'vertical angle' at which the wave arrives is from some direction other than the true one. This could also be caused by a distorted main lobe and/or excessively large side lobes for example, which incidentally are the same for receiving as for transmitting. Ionospheric anomalies are often capable of producing inconsistencies for which the blame is placed on an otherwise good aerial system.

One-way propagation paths

This may be the reason why the signal levels between two different stations a great distance apart are not of the same order (assuming more or less identical aerials, similar ground conditions, and that the same amount of radiated power is being used). Investigations offer no conclusive reason although there are several theories. For example, the propagated waves may not always take exactly the same paths, the result being considerable variation in signals received at one end or the other. A one-way path is also possible for one of the following reasons. Tilting of the ionospheric region, different MUF conditions at each end of the path, the presence of an ionized E region, and/or intense sporadic E at one end of the path and not at the other, and high, or very high D region absorption at either end of the path. When a one-

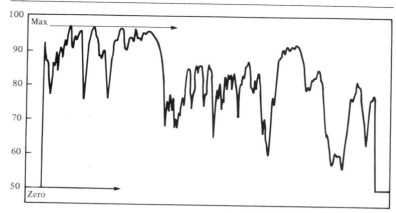

Figure 34   *Fading rate of F region primary echo at average virtual height of 300 kilometres. Duration of observation eight minutes. Dynamic range approximately 45 dB (receiver noise level to point of detector limiting)*

way path does occur, one end of it is usually in the dark part of the earth and the other in the illuminated part (daylight).

Fading

Variations in signal strength over a fairly long period and which may be rapid or slow, come under the general term of 'fading'. Often the receiver AVC will maintain the signal at a reasonably constant level except that background noise may increase when the signal fades and the receiver 'gain' is effectively increased. Fading can be expected during the day and on any frequency because wave absorption can change with the height of the sun above the horizon, and this, in turn, affects the electron density of the ionospheric region in use. There is also daily variation of the MUF, and if this falls below the frequency in use the received signal will fade, often disappearing completely (see Figure 34).

Ionization changes

The ionization of any part of an ionospheric region is in a continual state of change. There is also turbulence in the ionosphere, just as in the normal earth's atmosphere, even on seemingly quiet days and when the weather is fine. The amount of ionospheric absorption varies continually and radio waves entering a region at slightly different angles may be refracted differently. Also the polarization of a wave may be continually changed with refraction. So a radio wave arriving at the receiving aerial may have been influenced somewhat by ionospheric anomalies of one kind or another. For example, refracted waves may arrive at an aerial more or less in phase and at other times out of phase, the result being variations in signal strength, or fading.

Yet another example is 'selective fading' which causes severe modulation distortion on FM or AM when the carrier fades and the sidebands do not. (It is not so noticeable with single side-band transmissions.) It can be more serious at frequencies at or below about 4 MHz where the sidebands represent a larger percentage of the carrier frequency but is not so apparent at higher frequencies, e.g. 21 and 28 MHz.

Scatter propagation

From the explanations of ionospheric propagation given else-where, it might be expected that where a 'skip' zone exists, no signals would be heard, especially if the point of reception is beyond ground-wave coverage and of course too close to the place of transmission for ionospheric refracted signals to be received. At times signals are receivable under these conditions, although the strength is low and they have a characteristic 'fluttering' fade. This is due to the signals having been scattered so much that they arrive at the point of reception from random directions and with random phase relationships.

There are several different forms of scatter propagation which are sometimes of use in amateur radio. These are back scatter and side scatter, tropospheric and ionospheric scatter, and also 'trans-equatorial scatter. Tropospheric and trans-equatorial modes are considered to be forward-scatter modes of propagation. Tropospheric scatter is concerned only with VHF, but ionospheric back scatter is used in conjunction with F region ionospheric 'over-the-horizon' radar systems (see Chapter 6).

D, E and F region scatter

These regions are all useful for ionospheric scatter. Above the MUF, some signals get returned to earth by being scattered off

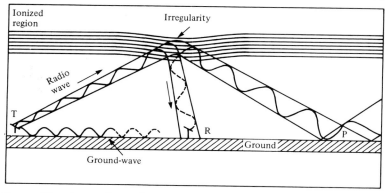

Figure 35   *Anomalies such as 'tilting' in an ionospheric region can cause scatter propagation. Signals from the transmitter* (T) *are propagated normally via the region to* (P) *and would continue in the same way. The irregularity in the ionized region changes the direction of some of the transmission to other points such as* (R)

irregularities in the ionospheric region. The signals may continue forward along the great circle path in the normal way but some may be returned in another direction as in Figure 35. Scatter signals are usually quite weak but the distances covered can be quite considerable when scatter is from the higher F region. Up to 2000 kilometres (1200 to 1300 miles) is possible even with E region scatter. This mode of propagation does, however, require great transmitting power and large efficient aerial systems and for this reason is not greatly used.

Side scatter and back scatter

Either mode involves some difficulties and the results are not always encouraging. Being ionospheric modes they have been included for the sake of completeness. It is of course possible to establish communication with some distance point, other than by normal ionospheric propagation over a direct great circle path. This is done by 'bouncing' a transmission from earth, via an ionospheric region which can also be reached in the same way from a distant point in a completely different direction, i.e. not a great circle direction. This involves directing beam aerials to a region capable of reasonably strong scatter. Again the signals are often weak and so more transmitting power may be required than is normal. There is very little fading but signals can exhibit a 'hollow' sound, or even an echo effect.

Side scatter propagation is closely related to back scatter, the main difference being that although the signals are 'bounced' from earth via an ionospheric region, they are scattered sideways instead of in a more or less reverse direction as with back scatter. Again optimum results are obtained by orientating beam aerials in the appropriate directions. Side scatter signals are often stronger and contacts have been obtained over distances of around 5000 kilometres (3000 miles) with this mode.

Trans-equatorial scatter

This mode is useful mainly for the higher range of frequencies, e.g. around 50 MHz, and although ionospheric, cannot be used for the normal HF bands or for VHF (2 metres for example).

More about sporadic E

In order to differentiate sporadic E from other E region phenomena it is usually designated 'Es'. Sporadic clouds form at a height about the same as that of the normal E region, i.e. around 100 kilometres. They vary in area and may last for only a few minutes or even several hours.

Es cloud ionization varies in density and the clouds move quite rapidly, generally in one direction, although they may drift in others. They occur mainly during the summer months, usually between May and August, but observations have shown that sporadic E can also occur during the winter months (October/November). In the southern hemisphere the seasonal occurrences are reversed.

The formation of sporadic E clouds is thought to be due to horizontal wind shears in the jetstreams that occur in the northern (or southern) hemisphere and which can produce ionization intense enough to propagate radio waves at frequencies as high as 145 MHz. Data from rockets used to penetrate sporadic E clouds have revealed high electron density, the wind velocities involved and height parameters. It is generally understood that because Es formation and ionization is associated with terrestrial or meteorological events, it is most unlikely that solar radiation, X-rays ultraviolet or gamma rays, which could not be focused long enough

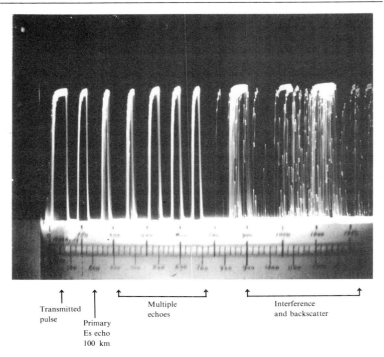

Figure 36   *Sporadic E (Es) observation. Photo shows transmitter pulse (right) followed by primary echo (125 kilometres), then five secondary echoes followed by random interference*

on relatively small and fast moving 'cloud' would be of any consequence. A typical sporadic E observation is shown in Figure 36. Because of the high density of ionization of the sporadic cloud at the time the photo was taken, the number of multiple, or secondary, echoes is quite high.

The MUF of Es clouds is a function of ionization intensity, and although the highest frequency that can be propagated from radio waves arriving at an oblique angle is not known, propagation at 200 MHz has often been reported. It is likely to occur more often at lower frequencies, e.g. 145 MHz and even as low as 27 MHz as CB radio enthusiasts have discovered, although this is usually only possible during the summer months. Propagation by Es is not particularly reliable because (a) it may only last for a short period and (b) the distances that can be covered depend entirely on the location and size of the cloud.

However, during the summer months when a number of Es

clouds may form in different areas, there are possibilities of DX on 145 MHz and even lower frequencies, and distances of well over 1600 kilometres (1000 miles) have been covered.

Meteor trails

When meteors enter the upper atmosphere they do so at very high speed and a large amount of energy is released by virtue of friction between the meteor and air as it slows down. Part of this energy can ionize the atmosphere along the path taken by the meteor and even a small one can produce an ionized path of considerable diameter and a mile or more in length. The ionized 'path' is often large enough to refract HF radio waves back to earth but as the ions quickly recombine, propagation may last for a very short period, often only a few seconds.

If a meteor trail lasts long enough, signals from stations that would not otherwise be received may, for one reason or another, be heard on amateur bands at frequencies ranging from 14 MHz to well into the VHF region.

Very often meteor showers may occur and these can become ionized to such an extent that it becomes possible to effect communication on 28 MHz for a considerable time. As with sporadic E, a well ionized meteor trail needs to be about midway between two stations attempting to establish contact by this medium. The angle of radiation from the transmitting aerial must be low enough for signals to be refracted.

Since meteor trail propagation is virtually a 'single hop' mode, maximum propagation distances may not be much over 1500 to 1600 kilometres (1000 miles or so).

Aurorae (borealis and australis)

This has already been mentioned and auroral propagation is possible at times on 28 MHz. Auroral activity is greater during magnetic storms and extends further south (or north from the southern polar regions). During these periods radio waves in the frequency range 3 to 5 MHz can be randomly reflected because an auroral curtain can become intensely ionized. VHF signals directed towards the auroras are returned in more or less the opposite direction depending on the angle incidence with the

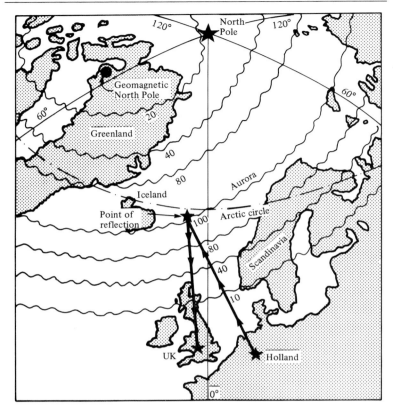

Figure 37 *Auroral curtain reflection (northern hemisphere). Contact established on VHF between a station in the UK and one in Holland. Signals may penetrate some way in before reflection occurs*

'curtain'. When such a condition prevails it is necessary to use directive aerials at each station and pointing in the direction of the curtain.

Most operational activity with auroral propagation is on the 2 metre band and an example of the propagation path between two stations, one in England and one in Holland, is illustrated in Figure 37.

Propagation via the aurorae produces a rapid flutter on signals, which themselves have a frequency between about 100 to 2000 Hz. This makes it difficult to read amplitude and frequency modulated transmissions. CW is therefore the preferred mode of communication.

Auroral curtain propagation occurs more often near the polar regions than at mid-latitudes but is non-existent in tropical regions. Peak times for this mode (in the northern hemisphere) are during March and September but it can occur at other times. An auroral display need not be visible in order to take advantage of it, although propagation can continue for several days (night and day).

Ionospheric storms

Disturbances in the ionosphere, usually called 'ionospheric storms', are due to eruptions on the sun. They are coincident with disturbances in the earth's magnetic field (magnetic storms) and are most frequent during a solar sunspot cycle maximum. Such storms are responsible for a reduction in the F2 critical frequencies and a large increase in D region absorption of HF radio waves. As a consequence the MUF may be lowered so that communication on the HF bands may prove to be impossible. Such storms vary in duration and intensity, lasting from one to several days. They tend to recur at intervals of 28 days (time of rotation of the sun) and are normally associated with one particular sunspot or a group.

Sudden ionospheric disturbances (SID)

There are times when HF communication may be interrupted, quite suddenly, by the event of solar flares from which the radiation levels (ultra-violet, and X-rays) are high enough to produce a marked increase in D region ionization, thus causing signals on the HF bands to completely disappear but return minutes, or sometimes hours, later.

N and M modes of propagation

Either mode can be observed during ionospheric sounding using pulse transmissions but can cause complications during normal long path radio wave transmissions. The 'N' mode is illustrated in Figure 38(a). A radio wave may first reach a sporadic E cloud and be reflected (or refracted) back to earth from which it is again

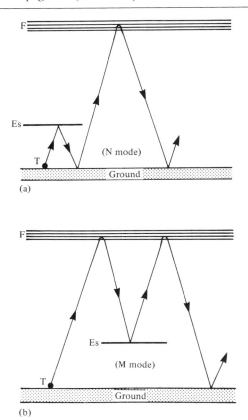

Figure 38   *(a) N mode of propagation. (b) M mode of propagation*

reflected, this time by-passing the Es directly to the F region, after which refraction from that region and reflection back from earth continues. There could be further occurrences of N mode propagation along the path of travel.

The 'M' mode of propagation Figure 38(b), is somewhat similar except that a radio wave may first reach the F region, be refracted and returned downward to a sporadic cloud from which it is refracted (or reflected) back to the F region. After this, propagation continues, F region to earth and back to F region and so on, along the path of travel. Both N and M modes could occur frequently along the path taken by a radio wave since sporadic E forms randomly in different areas as already described.

It should be mentioned here that intense sporadic E can prevent HF radio waves from reaching the F region altogether, usually for short periods (several minutes) but longer if the Es cloud is large. This is illustrated photographically in Figure 39(a) and (b).

Other ionospheric and solar cycle events

1 The eleven-year solar cycles and weather conditions

Some notes concerned with a possible direct relationship between the eleven-year solar cycles and weather conditions in Northern Europe dating from the Maunder minimum period (circa 1640–1714) to more recent times, were included at the beginning of Chapter 3. There is no need to repeat these but it remains that the weather conditions during the periods mentioned were extreme, with prolonged and very cold winters all over Europe and extending toward the Mediterranean area. Figure 22 (Chapter 3) and the dated periods speak for themselves.

2 Ionospheric conditions and weather

The following describes, albeit briefly, some experiments carried out in Eastern China and which stemmed from a report issued in 1936 by the Melbourne Radio Research Board. This dealt with the correlationship of ionospheric conditions and barometric pressure at ground level. The observations are concerned with sporadic E events as well as with normal E and F ionospheric regions. Low power pulse transmissions (20 watts) were used with simple aerial systems at frequencies between 6 and 7 MHz. Experiments were carried out over a period of three years by the Rev. E. Gherzi, at the time Director for Meteorology and Seismology at the Zi Ka Wei Observatory, Shanghai, China.

Armed with synoptic maps from the weather service, Gherzi discovered what he describes as the first coincidence between the presence of E or F region echoes and the 'air mass' which, at the time, was dominating the weather.

He found that every time the Pacific trade-wind air mass prevailed, all reflections were from the E region. When a Siberian air mass dominated the weather, then echoes were received from the F1 region. When tropical air was making the weather,

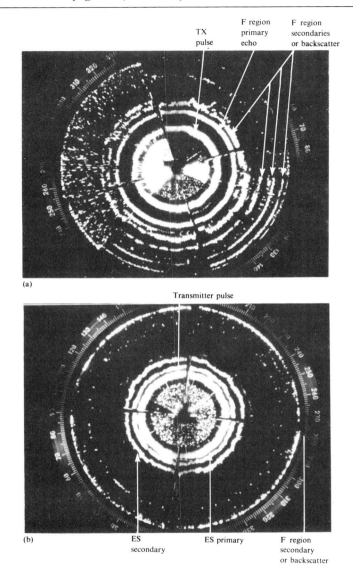

Figure 39 *Sporadic E and F region observations. Photographs taken from a special display. (a) F region echoes at 6.5 MHz. (b) Short time later, F region echoes blocked by sporadic E with exception of an F secondary. Note: First inner ring — transmitter pulse. Centre portion of display blank due to delay between start of timebase and initiation of transmitter pulse. Conditions reverted to original as in (a) after a few minutes*

returned echoes were from the F2 region. These conditions were observed for several years regardless of the month or the season. His article mentioned that the observations were actually used to produce weather forecasts which proved, as he put it, 'almost always excellent'. He goes on to describe in great detail, the possibilities of increasing the accuracy of weather forecasting in conjunction with ionospheric sounding and gives many quite convincing reasons for doing so.

3 Space shuttle: ionospheric disturbance

Extract from a report to NASA, December 1983

Effect of Columbia space shuttle travelling very close to, or within the boundaries, of the F region. Date Dec. 8th 1983. Pass time over East Anglia area UK, 1127 to 1138 GMT.

The report mentioned the possibility of a 'shock wave' created by the space shuttle and causing disturbance of the F region. It continued as follows:

Prior to the time of the pass (virtually overhead) the ionospheric F region virtual height was being continuously observed and recorded as 250 kilometres (approximately 160 miles). There was also a strong 'secondary echo' registered at 500 kilometres. Both the primary and secondary echoes were strong and reasonably constant in amplitude.

Time 1127 GMT. From this time onward and during the shuttle pass, the echoes from the F region began to appear from random virtual (?) heights during which strong echoes appeared from what was thought to be intense sporadic E (Es). Note that sporadic E is unusual at this time of the year. The F region echoes still appeared as though coming from random 'heights' and continued to do so for a period of 20 to 30 minutes after the shuttle pass over the area had ended at approximately 1138 GMT. Continued observation revealed that the 'sporadic E' (?) had disappeared and the F region echoes once again showed a virtual height as before, 250 kilometres.

Similar observations were made by other ionosonde stations and it was considered a strong possibility that a shock wave was created by the Columbia space shuttle since it was travelling at a speed of around 17,000 miles per hour and at a height above the earth that would put it within the upper and lower boundaries of the F2 region.

4   In Antarctica (circa 1957–8)

As part of the UK contribution to the International Geophysical Year (1957–8) a Union Radio ionosonde was set up at Halley Bay in Antarctica under the auspices of the Royal Society, London. The base was located on an ice shelf 170 metres thick which was slowly but continually moving. Both the climate and the location on the ice introduced a considerable number of problems with equipment and particularly the transmitting aerials.

However, apart from normal ionospheric sounding a 'non-ionospheric' feature was revealed. Firstly consistent gaps in ionospheric traces were observed and eventually interpreted as interference effects between radio waves which had travelled directly to, or from, the ionosonde aerials, and those that had travelled through the 170 metre thick ice shelf and were being reflected by the sea beneath. These observations and subsequent interpretation greatly contributed to the development of a new method for investigating ice sheets. The technique was called 'ice depth radio echo sounding' and has since been widely used by glaciologists of the British Antarctic Survey and a number of other groups. (A. S. Rodger, *British Antarctic Survey Bulletin No. 57*, 1982.) See Chapter 2 for details concerned with ionosondes.

References

1 *Ionospheric Radio Propagation*, K. Davies (Dover Publications).
2 *Climate. Past, Present and Future*, Prof. H. H. Lamb (2 vols), (Methuen).
3 *The ARRL Antenna Handbook*, Issue no. 15. 1974, The American Radio Relay League.
4 *The Amateur Radio Handbook*, RSGB, Third Edition, Nov. 1961.
5 'Ionospheric Reflections and Weather Forecasting in Eastern China', *Bulletin American Meteorological Society*, Rev. E. Gherzi, Vol. 27, Mar. 1946.
6 'Union Radio Ionosondes in Antarctica' (short notes), *British Antarctica Survey Bulletin*, A. S. Rodger, No. 54, 1982.
7 'Ionospheric Region disturbance by USA Space Shuttle Craft "Columbia"', *Orbit*, F. C. Judd, Dec. 8th 1983 (NASA). (Not published in UK.)

5 Ionospheric radar systems

Back scatter from the ionospheric region F1/F2 was dealt with in Chapter 4, and although little used for amateur radio communication, has been found applicable to what is called 'ionospheric radar'. The most notable of these systems is that developed for the USA Dept of Defense by the American General Electric Company. It is known as OTHR which stands for *over the horizon radar*. There are also forward scatter systems and the Soviet Union have what is believed to be an ionospheric pulsed radar system, better known to radio amateurs as the 'Woodpecker' because of the interference it can cause on HF amateur radio and broadcast bands. These systems employ enormous radiated power levels — in the region of 200 to 500 megawatts. The Russian system has been the subject of somewhat uninformed reports featured in radio broadcasts and television programmes.

The possibilities of ionospheric radar have been known for many years and may have stemmed from certain results obtained with an experimental high power Second World War radar system based on the CH (chain home) coastal radar that operated on frequencies around 26 to 28 MHz. Serious research on ionospheric radar began in the USA in about 1950. The origin of the Russian system is not known but they have had stations operating for a number of years.

The American OTHR system

The first of the American ionospheric radar systems known as 'Conus-B' was located in the State of Maine, near the town of Bangor, which is on the North-East American coast. Others are now operating on the East and West coasts. It is now known that ionospheric radar is being employed in the UK. Forward scatter HF radar has also been operating for some time in the Far East with receiving sites located in Western Europe and OTH radar is also being used in Australia.

However, to return to the American system, the term CONUS stands for Continental United States and the 'B' indicates it to be a back scatter system. While OTHR has certain disadvantages, it has other special advantages in that it can cover extremely wide areas by comparison with normal microwave radar, and is estimated to be far less costly than space orbiting radar equipment. OTHR is capable of tracking aircraft and ballistic missiles both from and to ground level and can therefore detect an actual missile launch as well as aircraft take off. It can also be employed to provide warnings of the approach of high winds (hurricanes), the location of weather fronts, very rough seas and even the movement of large ships at sea.

The development of OTHR

Many things had to be considered before a full-power OTHR system could be used. For example environmental problems such as potential electro-magnetic interference. This included possible material damage to persons in close proximity to the transmitting aerials even though initial experiments were carried out using only 100 megawatts of power. There were also considerable problems in developing special computer techniques.

OTHR depends on the special properties of the ionosphere and operates within the radio frequency spectrum from about 3 to 30 MHz. The F2 region is the only ionospheric region that can be used with this frequency range and with the specific angles of radiation from the aerials used for transmitting as well the requirements of the separate receiving aerials.

Microwave radar signals are not reflected by the ionospheric regions and travel straight through, hence their usefulness in communicating with satellites and radar tracking space vehicles high above the ionospheric regions. With OTHR a significant amount of radiation travels forward, as with any normal radio signal, but some is returned along a reciprocal path and this is known as 'back scatter'. The 'ionospheric' path taken by an OTHR signal and its reflection from a target, is illustrated in Figure 40. Most of the returned signals consist of ground or sea

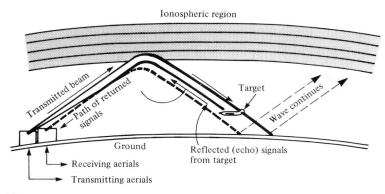

Figure 40   *Basic principle of OTHR*

clutter, but solid obstacles such as aircraft and ships that are in motion, generate discrete 'echoes' which, with Doppler processing, can be separated from the clutter.

Energy propagated beyond the first point of back scatter does of course travel on for another ionospheric 'hop', and whilst back scatter from this second hop could be used to extend the range of OTHR to something like 6670 kilometres (3600 nautical miles), the detection of aircraft and missiles etc. at that distance is not reliable.

How OTHR operates

What follows is a description of the CONUS-B OTHR station operating in the State of Maine in the USA, and the area it can cover. Other CONUS-B stations function in the same way and cover areas of similar size. The CONUS-B OTHR, the first of its kind, and set up in the State of Maine, was to detect airborne strategic bombers and cruise missiles that might be directed, in this case, toward the North American mainland.

The warning time with CONUS-B radar is a little over three hours for attacks at subsonic speed and just over one hour for attacks at supersonic speed. The effective detection range is around 3336 kilometres, or approximately 1800 nautical miles. The warning time with other radar systems is between ten and twenty minutes. The OTHR system in Maine covers a wide arc of approach detection (ARC-COV) as illustrated by Figure 41, which also shows the normal commercial airlines' Atlantic routes and the

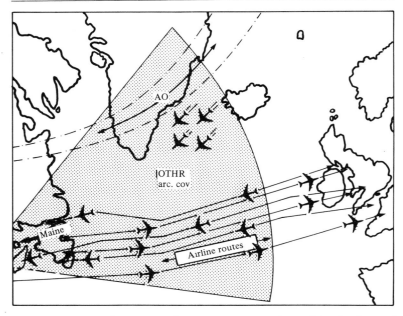

Figure 41   *Arc of coverage of an OTHR system located in the State of Maine, USA. Aurora Oval (AO)*

Auroral Oval (AO). This enormous arc is not covered simultaneously, but in sections.

The CONUS-B over the horizon radar system 414L is a bi-static radar, i.e. it has separate transmit and receive operations sites. Those located in Maine are shown in Figure 42. The transmit site is near Moscow/Caratunk, the combined receive operations being located near Columbia Falls, also in Maine. In order to continuously adapt in real time to the prevailing ionospheric conditions, both the transmit and receive functions are completely computer controlled. Operation of the transmit and receive operations sites is synchronized in absolute time to better than one microsecond accuracy by Loran C which eliminates the need for communicating highly accurate timing information between the sites.

Normal mode of operation

The normal mode establishes a surveillance barrier up to 30 degrees wide and anywhere within the 60 degree azimuth sector

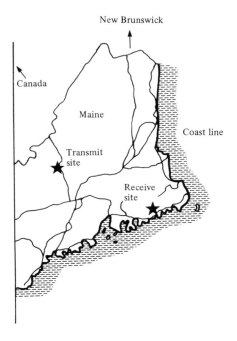

Figure 42   *Location of OTHR transmit and receive sites in the State of Maine, USA*

as shown in Figure 43(a). The technique used to illuminate this barrier is a 'step-scan', on a regular periodic basis, for sequential illumination of four contiguous range azimuth sectors as in Figure 43(b).

Each range azimuth sector normally covers a 7.5 degree by 500 nautical miles area; thus four sectors form the 30 degree barrier. Four parallel receive beams, with 2.5 degree centre spacings, are formed to correspond with each 7.5 degree range azimuth sector, and collect the energy reflected from targets in the coverage area (see Figure 43(c)). The beginning range for each range azimuth sector in the barrier can be independently chosen. The scan parameters are selectable to adapt the radar to the prevailing air traffic and propagation conditions in order to maximize target detectability.

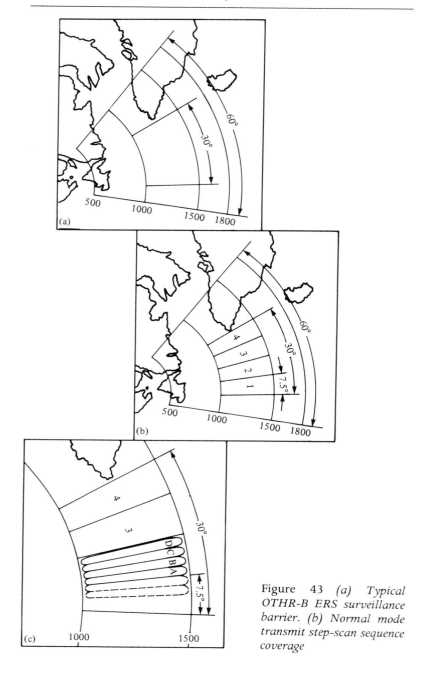

Figure 43 *(a) Typical OTHR-B ERS surveillance barrier. (b) Normal mode transmit step-scan sequence coverage*

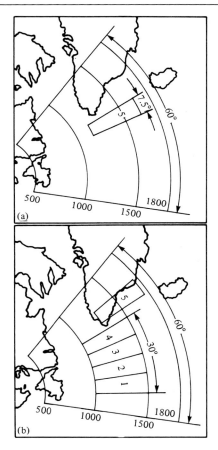

Figure 44 *(a) Interrogate mode azimuth sector. (b) Interleaved mode transmit step-scan sequence*

Interrogate mode

The interrogate mode, as in Figure 44(a), illuminates one particular range azimuth sector. It can be positioned independently anywhere within the 60 degree azimuth by 500 to 1800 nautical miles range capability of the radar system. The interrogate range azimuth sector is illuminated by contiguous coherent 'dwells' (in short pause). Again, all four parallel receive beams, spaced on 2.5 degree fixed centres, collect the reflected target energy. In addition, special high-resolution radar parameters are also available. All other radar operating parameters available in the normal mode, are also available in the interrogate mode. The interrogate mode is a special mode intended to provide extra detection energy, contiguous illumination, and high range velocity and azimuth resolution. It is used in special, or suspicious situations, to enhance the characterization of particular targets, e.g. for 'flight size' measurement.

Interleaved mode

The interleaved mode combines the interrogate and normal modes as in Figure 44(b). One interrogate mode 'dwell' is provided after each full scan of the normal barrier. Separate radar operating parameters can be independently selected for the interrogate and normal mode portions of the scan. This mode allows barrier surveillance to be retained while focusing on special target situations anywhere in the 60 degrees by 500 to 1800 nautical mile coverage region.

Frequency range

The operating frequency range is 6.7 to 22.3 MHz, selectable in 1 Hz increments. In the normal mode, a common operating frequency for all range azimuth sectors within the surveillance barrier is chosen. An FM/CW waveform is used. Waveform bandwidths of 2.5, 5, 10, and 100 Hz, and waveform repetition frequencies (WRFs) of 20, 30, 45 and 60 Hz can be selected.

Radar functions

By using CW rather than pulses (as in normal radar systems and for ionospheric sounding) the CONUS-B system minimizes radio interference. The relatively wide (7.5 degree) transmit beams, overlayed with four parallel narrow (2.5 degree) receive beams result in the most cost effective method to achieve the high detection energies and resolution required for successful operation.

   Remote transponders are also part of the system. These provide information for accurately converting target positions, measured in radar coordinates (as effected by propagation through the

Figure 45   *An OTHR transmitting aerial array (see text for details)*

ionosphere) to geographical coordinates, i.e. to latitude and longitude.

Transmitting aerial system

An OTHR transmitting aerial as shown in Figure 45, consists of four separate side-by-side 12-element sub-arrays, each optimized to cover a different portion of the total operating frequency range. Together they provide the capability to operate anywhere in the 6.7 to 22.3 MHz frequency range and present low VSWRs to the transmitters at all scan angles. The highest frequency sub-array (Band E) uses vertical dipole elements while the other three sub-arrays (bands B, C and D) employ 'canted' dipoles. This arrangement provides elevation patterns which match that required for propagation to the desired ranges via ionospheric refraction. The elements are mounted in front of a common back screen ranging from 45 to 100 feet high and approximately 2265 feet long. A common ground screen extends 750 feet in front of the whole length of the arrays.

The transmitters

Twelve transmitters operate simultaneously into the 12-elements of a selected aerial sub-array. Each transmitter contains four band-tuned tank circuits which respectively match the four sub-arrays, and produce up to 100 kilowatts average power, with extremely high spectral purity, at any operating frequency between 6.7 and 22.3 MHz. A 100-kilowatt water-cooled tetrode is used in the final high power amplifier stage of each transmitter. The twelve transmitters are driven by a 'beam former' at low power level, which causes the transmitter/array to collimate the desired 7.5 degree beam and steer it to the selected positions. In operation the transmit site generates up to 100 megawatts of effective radiated power.

The receive function

The receiving aerial system is a broadside array consisting of 137 fan monopole elements mounted in front of a back screen 3906 feet long and 50 feet high. The same form of ground screen is used, extending 750 feet in front of the array and along its full length. Two bands are used to cover the 6.7 to 22.3 MHz operating frequency range – low band, 6.7 to 11.12 MHz and the high band 11.12 to 22.3 MHz. On the low band every other element is used across the array giving a total of 68 active elements. In the high band, the centre 82 elements are used. Dividing the array in this fashion and using variable aperture weights in beam forming, results in virtually constant receive beam widths of 2.75 degrees, with no grating lobes over the full 60 degree azimuth coverage. The active receive elements are appropriately fed via buried co-axial lines to elemental receivers, one for each active element, for a total of 82.

Each elemental receiver employs 16 RF pre-selectors to cover from 6.7 to 22.3 MHz. The receivers are high dynamic range, matched units, which are computer controlled. In each receiver, the signals are amplified, filtered, translated to baseband (I and Q) and digitized to 15-bit words. These digital words are passed to the beam former/signal processor group. The beam former combines the digitized outputs to form four simultaneous receive beams spatially coincident with the illuminated range-azimuth sector. This four-beam cluster step scans synchronously with the transmit beam. Beam width, beam spacing, pointing angle and correction for frequency and real time measured receive subsystem errors, are controlled by the receive control computer. The signal processor processes the four receive beams virtually simultaneously. The information in each beam is resolved into 4096 range and Doppler cells. Signal processor functions include moving target indicator (MTI), interference suppression, range and Doppler resolution processing, non-coherent integration, peak detection and parameter estimation. All signal processor function commands, mode controls and set-up data are provided by the receive control computer which is also used for radar control and monitoring.

The operations functions

The operations function is also located at the receive/operations site and consists of a UNIVAC 1110 data processor with peripherals, the radar control and display group, and the communications group. The UNIVAC data processor provides the primary processing resources for automatic detection/tracking, automatic correlation/indentification data recording and display/operator interfaces.

The radar control and display group consists of four alphanumeric terminals, three high resolution detection/tracking (D/T) display consoles, a correlation/identification (C/I) display console, a performance assessment (PA) display console, two hard copy units and a display monitor. Other displays interface to a U1110 computer through the display controller.

There are three high resolution graphic detection/tracking (D/T) consoles (see Figure 46) each with the capability to display both gray scale (i.e. intensity modulated radar and track data proportional to signal amplitude) and tabular information. There is also a performance assessment console with gray scale capability that presents the spectrum monitor receiver output for channel selection, received clutter analysis, coordinate registration support and HF transponder data analysis. The console is used to monitor the HF propagation environment and provide information regarding the radar operating parameters needed to maintain the desired coverage.

Two hard copy units provide printed information presented by either of the D/T, C/I, or P/A consoles. In addition to the above

Figure 46   *OTHR control and display consoles (see text for details)*

described radar detection features, the system employs a dedicated FM/CW back-scatter sounder. Inputs from two remote vertical sounders are also used to assess ionospheric propagation conditions in real time. (This is similar to a pulse ionosonde system except that a different form of modulation is used.)

OTHR tracking

Two examples are given (Figure 47) which show (a) a track from a subsonic aircraft and (b) the track of a supersonic aircraft, in this case the Concorde, at one stage travelling at a ground speed of 1176 knots at a distance from the OTHR of 1207 nautical miles.

Before dealing with the Russian ionospheric radar system some further notes on the American OTHR system may be of interest. Interference to an OTHR either on, or close to the frequency of operation is accepted by the system as a form of noise regardless of its origin or nature. Special circuitry is incorporated to convert interfering carriers, irrespective of how they are modulated, to

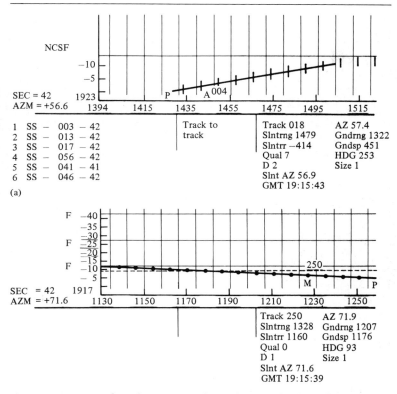

Figure 47 *Examples of OTHR tracking. (a) Track of a subsonic speed aircraft. (b) Track of a Concorde supersonic speed aircraft across the Atlantic (see text for details)*

relatively unharmful broad band noise. The policy of the American Department of Defense as far as interference from their OTHRs is concerned, is to cause as little as possible. Very high power is used only when ionospheric conditions are poor or if the level of static (from storm lightning) is very high.

OTHR coverage and the ionosphere

OTHR relies entirely upon ionospheric conditions, hence the wide frequency range it needs for full operation at all times. The F region plays the most important role which, together with the complex aerial systems, permit such an enormous area of coverage. As a final illustration of how the transmit beams are

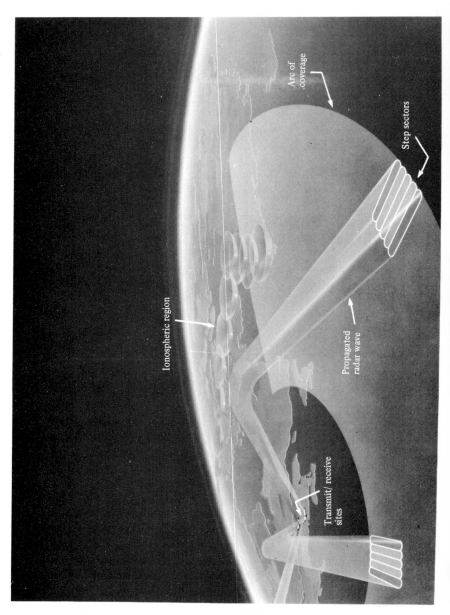

Figure 48 *An artist's impression of OTHR beams, the area of coverage and the beam reflection from an ionospheric region*

reflected from the ionospheric region and can be moved as described, an artist's impression is included (Figure 48). The artist has created a 'looking down from space' view, which, it is hoped, will provide the reader with a better visualization, not only of the wide arc of coverage but the great distances over which OTHR is effective. As already mentioned, the foregoing description of the OTHR station in Maine applies to the remainder now operating in the USA.

The Russian system

There are probably very few amateur radio HF band operators anywhere in the world who have not experienced interference from what are believed to be Russian ionospheric radar systems. Because of the low pulse recurrence frequency the transmissions produce a strong audible 'tock-tock' sound at whatever frequencies are being used. The somewhat appropriate name given to these transmissions is the 'Woodpecker'. There are at least three of these transmitters in operation, possibly more, although with the approach of the solar cycle minimum (1986) they have not been heard so often as during the maximum period of the cycle (no. 21) circa 1980.

It is not known for certain whether the Russian 'Woodpecker' transmissions are pure radar, i.e. used for the location of aircraft and/or ballistic missiles, or to locate and communicate with satellites. A low pulse recurrence frequency, ten per second with a pulse width of about four milliseconds is generally used, although these parameters are sometimes changed, often during an actual transmission.

Very little technical information concerned with the 'Woodpecker' has been available from Russian or other sources. The British media, particularly television, have from time to time given entirely misleading conceptions of what the transmissions are and what they are supposed to be capable of doing.

With the aid of special equipment, the author decided to carry out an investigation, which lasted about a year. The results were published in a technical journal after being vetted by the MOD (see references at the end of this chapter).

Like the American OTHR, the Russian system operates over a wide range of frequencies, and the effective radiated power is in the region 200 to 400 megawatts (confirmed). The signals do not

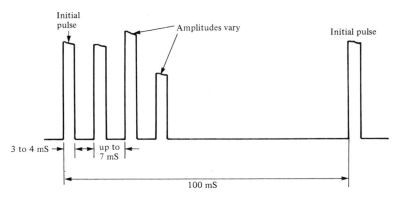

Figure 49   *Four pulse (Russian system) sequence (unmodulated) (see text and Figure 51)*

always have the same format as will be illustrated, although the pulse interval is always maintained at 100 milliseconds. For example, prior to most transmissions there are often a few seconds of 'unmodulated' multiple pulses as illustrated in Figure 49. These can appear on any frequency and could be alerting signals of some kind. It was discovered later that 'single' pulse signals carried a form of modulation. However, the true nature of any of the signals cannot be resolved without using (a) a receiver with a wide band frequency response, and (b) a wideband oscilloscope.

Analysis of 'Woodpecker' signals

Initial investigation began by examining the waveform of a 'Woodpecker' signal at the intermediate frequency stages output of a normal communications receiver (IF frequency 465 kHz). This revealed the pulse nature of the signal and what appeared to be an 'echo' as shown in Figure 50. There were also indications of some form of modulation on the primary (transmitted) pulse and the 'echo'. Rectification of the signal produced only barely visible signs of this modulation; probably due to capacitance in the detector circuitry. Wide band assessment was needed and this proved to be the answer.

Accordingly a receiver was modified to provide a through bandwidth of about 2 MHz. The oscilloscope bandwidth was 10 MHz. The receiver covered the whole frequency range known to be used by the Russian transmitters, this being from about

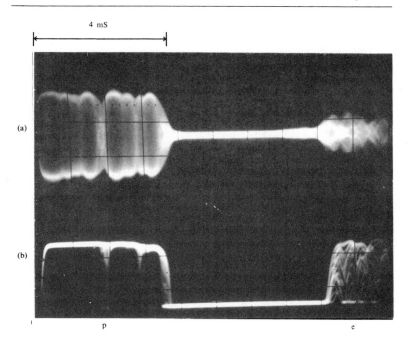

4 mS

(a)

(b)

p

e

Key

p Initial pulse with width of 4 milliseconds
e Echo (?) or respond signal initiated by radar pulse

Figure 50   *Russian 'Woodpecker' pulse signal (a) before detection (IF stages output). (b) After detection*

6.5 MHz to nearly 30 MHz. (It should be noted that the pulse signals shown in Figure 49 were resolved with the modified receiver as above.)

In the meantime a report had been published to the effect that the transmitted pulses were modulated with encoded information and which proved to be correct, as we shall see. Further it was found that the four pulse signals (Figure 49) were sometimes modulated, as can be seen in the oscillogram Figure 51.

Continuous observation revealed many different aspects of these transmissions, although the format of PRF and pulse width, with single pulse signals, remained substantially the same as dozens of oscillograms revealed. For example the oscillogram Figure 52(a) shows what appears to be scatter signals following the primary pulse, and then a large 'echo' coming from what

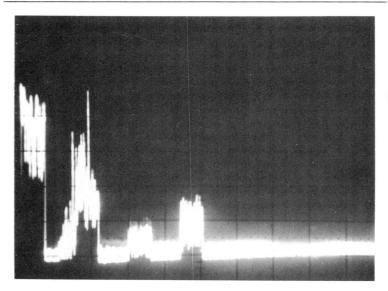

Figure 51   *Oscillogram of four pulse signals with modulation on each pulse (see also Figure 53)*

would be a considerable distance, since the time lapse (primary pulse to echo) is 40 milliseconds. Assuming this to be a real echo from a fixed object (its time/distance did not vary) then the distance from the transmitter would have been $3000 \times 20 = 60,000$ kilometres (30,000 miles) and which suggests that the received echo had travelled around the earth by a long path.

In fact echoes that had apparently covered long distance paths were frequently observed as illustrated by the oscillogram Figure 52(b). One appears at about 90 milliseconds and yet there is one at less than 10 milliseconds.

Interference to amateur radio

Around the peak of solar cycle no. 21 these Russian pulse transmissions caused considerable interference on the amateur radio HF bands, particularly as the frequency of operation appeared to change almost randomly. This suggested that the best ionospheric conditions were continually being sought, probably with a frequency scanning ionospheric sounder linked in some way with the Woodpecker system. With some amateur receivers a

100 mS

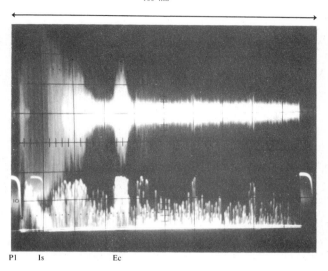

P1   Is   Ec

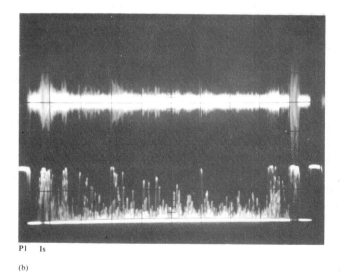

P1   Is

(b)

Key
P1   Initial transmitted pulse
Is   Scatter signals
Ec   Echo and/or telemetry signal

Figure 52   *(a) See text for description. (b) Similar to (a) with two distinct echoes (e) at about 10 and 80/90 milliseconds respectively*

4 mS

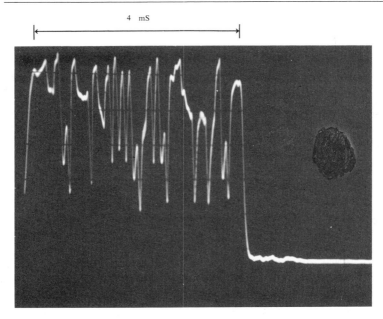

Figure 53 *Expanded oscillogram to show transmitted pulse with modulated 'code' (?) signals*

built-in noise blanker could reduce or eliminate the signals. Many radio amateurs tried to jam the signals by putting out transmissions on the frequency in use. This would have made no difference since systems of this nature, like the American OTHR, employ special circuitry in the receiving equipment to overcome such problems.

It remains however, that the Woodpecker transmitters may well begin operating again when ionospheric conditions become more stable, after the minimum of solar cycle no. 21 has passed and cycle no. 22 begins to climb toward its maximum.

Coded information

It was mentioned earlier that on most transmissions, where a single pulse was used with a PRF of ten per second, that the pulse itself was modulated with what were believed to be 'code' signals of some description. An 'expanded' oscillogram, Figure 53, shows this quite clearly. During reception these modulated signals

Over the horizon radar (OTH)

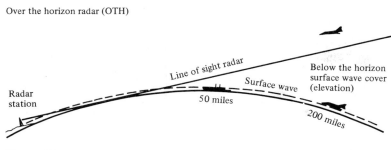

Figure 54

changed almost continuously, which suggested some form of 'control' information, possibly to satellites, or for transmission identification, or to provide specific information for receiving and/or other transmitting stations.

Whatever the real purpose of the Woodpecker transmissions, they were not used for controlling the weather in Russia or anywhere else, as mentioned on certain British television programmes, neither were they being used to create 'physiological' or 'psychological' effects, also a theory put forward on television and by other less informed media.

British OTHR system

A new OTHR system has been developed by Marconi Radar Systems of Chelmsford in Essex, which represents a major attribute to coastal and shipborne air defence.

The mode of propagation is 'surface-wave' but the system operates only over a sea path. However, it is capable of detecting low flying aircraft (at virtually wave-top height), sea skimming cruise missiles and ships at ranges of up to 200 miles, compared with 50 miles or so using conventional microwave radar, and as illustrated in Figure 54. The theory behind the design of a radar system that would not be limited by the natural curvature of the earth has been known for a long time. G. Marconi predicted the possibility as early as 1925 and it was known that Second World War Chain Home (CH) Radar Stations were ideally suited for the purpose but the computing power needed to extract weak target signals from the large amount of 'clutter' and other interference present had yet to be developed.

The Marconi OTHR employs an advanced signal processing unit with a functional capacity of 2000 million operations per second! Information regarding this and operational frequencies is classified except that the latter will be somewhere within the HF spectrum, e.g. 5 to 30 MHz. The same applies to transmitter power which will undoubtedly be high as with other OTHR systems.

Thanks are due to Marconi Radar Systems for information contained in the foregoing paragraphs.

References

1 *Back Scatter Ionospheric Sounding*, Kabanov and Oestrov (The Soviet Press 1965).
2 'Beyond the Far Horizon', *USAF Ionospheric Radar* (Interavia 1982).
3 'Over the Horizon Radar in the HF Band', Headrick and Solniik, *IEEE Journal*, Vol. 62, 1974.
4 'Jane's Weapons Systems', 1979–80 Edition, *Jane's Year Books* (McDonald and Jane's).
5 'Beyond the Blue Horizon' (OTH Radar), *Practical Wireless*, F. C. Judd, Aug. 1983.
6 *Over the Horizon Ionospheric Radar*, QST, April 1980.

The author is indebted to the USA Department of Defense and the American General Electric Company for permission to use the diagrams and photos kindly supplied by them.

6 The transmitting aerial and propagation

The performance of a transmitting aerial, and particularly its vertical angle directive properties, play a great part in ionospheric radio wave propagation. Most aerials used by radio amateurs are low in height in terms of wavelength with respect to the frequency of operation. This does unfortunately mean that maximum radiation may be at high vertical angles, even on the higher frequency bands. Where the height of the aerial in terms of wavelength is very low, the vertical angle of maximum radiation may be in the region of 70 to 80 degrees. For example, a half-wave aerial operating at 3.5 MHz at a physical height of say 40 feet (about 12 metres), has a height in terms of wavelength with respect to frequency of only $12/80 = 0.15$ wavelength. On the other hand a half-wave aerial operating on 14 MHz at the same physical height of 40 feet (12 metres) has a height in terms of wavelength of 20/40 or 0.5 (half a wavelength). The vertical angle of maximum radiation would in this case be much lower, in the region of 30 to 40 degrees, depending on the conductivity of the ground beneath.

Reflection from the ground

The performance of an aerial, particularly with respect to its directive properties, is considerably modified by the ground beneath it. The earth behaves as a large reflector for those waves that are radiated from the aerial at angles lower than the horizon. The downward travelling waves are reflected by the ground with the angle of reflection being the same as the angle of incidence so that a wave meeting the ground at an angle of say, 15 degrees, is reflected upward at the same angle.

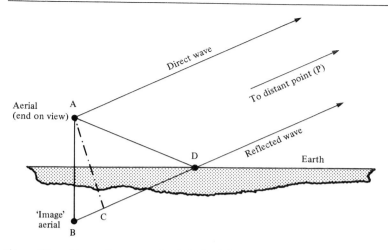

Figure 55   *At any distance point (P), the field strength will be the resultant of two waves, one direct from the aerial and the other reflected from earth. The reflected wave travels a greater distance than the direct wave by an amount (BC) where the reflected wave is considered to originate at the phantom or image aerial (see text)*

Waves reflected in this manner combine with the direct waves radiated at angles above the horizon in various ways depending on the orientation of the aerial with respect to ground, its length, and the conductivity characteristics of the ground. At some vertical angles above the horizontal, the direct and reflected waves may be exactly in phase, which means that the maximum field strengths of both waves are reached at the same time and at the same place, and the direction of the fields are the same. In this case the resultant field strength is equal to the sum of the two.

At other vertical angles the two waves may be completely out of phase which means that the fields are maximum but the directions are opposite at the same place. The resultant field strength in this case is the 'difference' between the two. At other angles the resultant fields will have other values in amplitudes, i.e. between a maximum 'in-phase value' and a minimum 'out of phase value'. Thus the effect of the earth is to increase the intensity of radiation at some vertical angles and decrease it at others.

The effect of reflection from earth is illustrated in Figure 55. At a sufficiently large distance two waves converging at a distant point can be considered to be in parallel. The 'reflected' wave

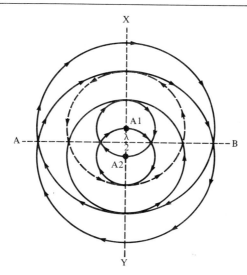

Figure 56   *Interference between waves from two separated aerials (A1 and A2) causes the directivity to change from that otherwise obtained from a single aerial. In this case two aerials are separated by a half-wavelength. The radiation fields from the two cancel along the line (X–Y) but, at distances which are large compared with the space between two aerials, add together along the line (A–B). The radiation field resulting from this decreases uniformly as the line is orientated through intermediate positions from (A–B) to (X–Y)*

does however travel a greater distance to reach the point (*p*) than does a direct wave. It is this difference in path length that accounts for the effects described in the previous paragraphs.

If the earth were a perfect conductor, reflection would take place without a change in phase if the waves were vertically polarized. If a 'horizontally' polarized wave were reflected under similar conditions, there would be a complete reversal of phase (180 degrees). However, the earth is not a perfect conductor but for practical purposes is assumed to be so for calculating the vertical angle radiation patterns of aerials. The error introduced is small enough to be of little consequence except at very low vertical angles.

For example, when the path of a reflected wave is exactly half a wavelength longer than that of the direct wave, the two waves will arrive out of phase if the polarization of the wave is vertical. This corresponds to the condition along the line X − Y as illustrated by Figure 56. If the path of the reflected wave is a

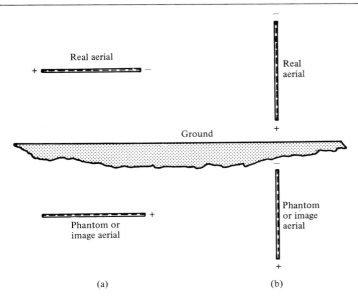

Figure 57 *Horizontal and vertical aerials, each a half-wave in length, and the earth images (see text)*

complete wavelength longer than that of the direct wave, then both arrive in-phase.

The aerial image

We can use the concept of an 'image' aerial to show the effect of reflection as in Figure 55. The reflected wave has the same path length (AD equal to BD) that would be created if there were a second aerial having the same characteristics as the real aerial but located below the earth at a depth equal to the height of the real aerial above. Just like an image in a mirror, the 'phantom' aerial is in reverse as illustrated in Figure 57. One of the real aerials (a) is horizontal and is charged instantaneously so that one end is positive and the other negative. The phantom aerial, also horizontal, has opposite polarity. On the other hand, if a 'vertical' half-wave aerial (b) is charged positively at one end (the end nearest earth in this case) then the far end of the 'phantom' aerial will also be charged positively. In this instance the currents flowing in both the real and phantom aerials will be in the same

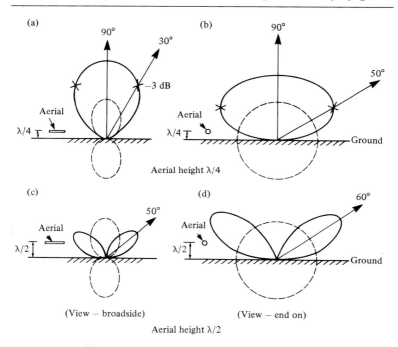

Figure 58 *Effect of the earth on the vertical angle radiation from a horizontal half-wave aerial for heights, of (a–b), 0.25 and (c–d), 0.5 wavelength. The dotted line patterns are those that would be obtained with the aerials in 'free-space', i.e. with no reflection from earth*

direction, i.e. in-phase. By using a technique similar to that for determining the radiation patterns of aerials with more than one active element (Figure 56) it becomes possible to obtain a close approximation of the vertical angle pattern of an aerial produced as a result of reflection of its radiation from the earth beneath. Figure 58(a), (b), (c) and (d) show how the 'pattern' of the vertical angle radiation is modified by the proximity of earth, or to put it another way, by the height of the aerial above earth. An aerial would have to be located in virtually 'free-space' before it could produce its 'natural' radiation pattern in both the vertical and horizontal modes, i.e. at such a height in terms of wavelength, that there would be practically no reflection from the earth beneath. Few radio amateurs can meet this requirement except with aerials operating at VHF and at a height of several wavelengths above earth. It must be emphasized that the patterns shown in Figure 58 are idealistic and may only be approximated in practice.

Nevertheless, some idea of the vertical angle radiation is of value, even if known only approximately. The ideal would be to have maximum vertical angle radiation virtually parallel to ground, or at least to within 10 to 15 degrees so that maximum radiation takes a path tangential, or nearly so, to the surface of the earth thus ensuring the longest possible first 'ionospheric hop'.

Figure 57, which is almost to scale with reference to the radius of the earth and a virtual F region height of 350 to 400 kilometres, shows that a radio wave propagated tangentially to the surface of the earth, will have maximum 'hop' distances of about 4000 kilometres. It must be remembered however, that in illustrations of this nature the 'lines' of propagation really only represent the path of absolute maximum radiation from an aerial. The radiated field from a transmitting aerial continues to expand all the way along its total path of travel as will be illustrated later.

The so-called 'hop' distances are determined by the vertical angle of maximum radiation from an aerial and the virtual height of an ionospheric region. Maximum radiation at vertical angles from aerials operating at frequencies within the amateur radio HF bands depends, as already mentioned, on the height of the aerial above earth. However, the earth itself can also behave as a fairly efficient 'plane' reflector. For example, with a horizontal half-wave aerial at a height of a quarter-wavelength above earth, the aerial itself can behave like a 'driven element' above a plane reflector of infinite area, rather like a dipole and parasitic reflector, except that maximum radiation is in an upward direction, i.e. at an angle of 90 degrees to the plane of the earth as shown in Figure 58(a) and (b).

If the conductivity of the earth beneath is reasonably good the 'gain' in radiated power at the angle of maximum will be in the region of 3 dB over an otherwise 'free-space' dipole. This can be both advantageous and disadvantageous depending on the frequency band in use.

Ground reflection factor

The condition mentioned in the previous paragraph can be based on a ground reflection factor of 2 with the angle of maximum radiation θ derived from arc sin $(A/4h)$, where θ is the wave angle, h the height of the aerial in wavelength (with respect to the

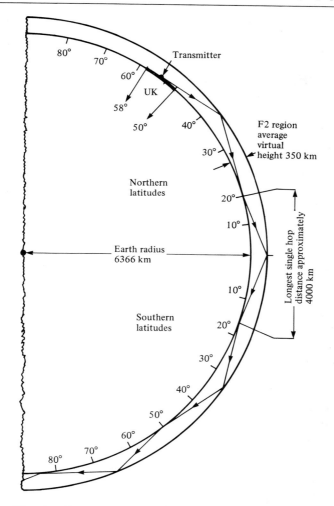

Figure 59 *A radio wave propagated tangentially to the surface of the earth will cover the longest 'hop' distance of about 4000 kilometres. Illustration almost to scale (see text)*

frequency of operation) and *A* has a value of 1. For the example Figure 58(a):

arc sin $\left(\frac{1}{4} \times 0.25\right)$

gives maximum vertical angle radiation at 90 degrees.

111

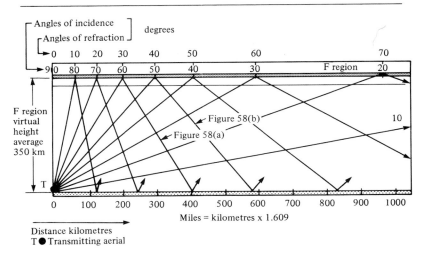

Figure 60   *Angles of incidence and angles of refraction relative to vertical angles of radiation from an aerial. Distances in kilometres covered for various angles of refraction based on 2 (tan $\theta \times 350$) where θ is angle of refraction and 350 is mean virtual height of F region in kilometres. Angle of refraction = 90 minus angle of incidence*

Angles of incidence

The 'amplitude' of radiation at different vertical angles can also be related to angles of incidence with an ionospheric region and from which a good approximation of propagation distances can be obtained, as illustrated in Figure 60. For example, with vertical incidence at 90 degrees, a wave reflected from the F region with a virtual height of 350 kilometres, will be returned to earth at the point from which it originated (the basis of ionospheric sounding). For the same region virtual height, and for all other wave angles, a wave will be refracted and returned at a finite distance. If we take a condition as in Figure 58(a) (view broadside to the aerial) the angle between 90 and 60 degrees (the latter cutting the -3 dB point of the radiation pattern) will be 30 degrees. The wave at this angle will be refracted and reach earth at a distance equal to:

$$2(\tan 30 \times 350)$$

which is 404 kilometres, or the first 'hop' distance. For an 'end-on' view, as in Figure 58(b) the angle between 90 degrees and the line

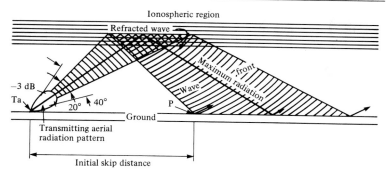

Figure 61 *Illustrates how a radiated wave expands more and more as the distance from the aerial increases. Note: For convenience of illustration the angles of radiation are limited to the − 3 dB points of the vertical angle radiation pattern of the aerial*

(50 degrees) which stems from the − 3 dB point on the aerial radiation pattern, gives 40 degrees. The distance at which the wave will reach earth following refraction from the ionospheric region will be:

$$2(\tan 40 \times 350)$$

which is 587 kilometres.

Remember that reflection, or refraction, of the wave depends on the frequency in use and the ionospheric region critical frequency.

However, radio waves do not travel as thin straight lines, and diagrams that illustrate propagation in this way are really only showing the absolute maximum of the radiated wave from the aerial as it follows the path of propagation.

Although such diagrams are commonly used, they do not indicate that a radiated wave expands more and more after it leaves the aerial, whether propagated via an ionospheric region, or as a point-to-point ground-wave. For this reason the illustration Figure 61 has been produced. Although the 'beamwidth' of the aerial radiation pattern at − 3 dB is 40 degrees, this has been narrowed down to 20 degrees to clarify the illustration. Even so it is not difficult to visualize how much the radiated field has expanded, even by the first 'hop'. This expansion continues along the whole path of propagation. This also means that there is really only one skip region, between the source of transmission (*Ta*) and the first point (*p*), where the wave reaches earth after being returned from an ionospheric region.

113

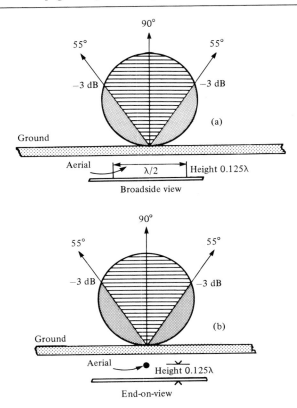

Figure 62 *Nominal vertical angle radiation patterns of a half-wave aerial a quarter wavelength above ground. (a) Broadside view. (b) End-on view*

Omni-directional ionospheric propagation

As we have seen, aerials of low height, in terms of wavelength, have very high vertical angles of radiation with maximum at virtually 90 degrees, but this could be advantageous in a particular way, since the main pattern of radiation will be fairly broad at the − 3 dB points. For example, the radiation patterns shown in Figure 62(a) and (b) could result from a half-wave aerial operating on 3.5 MHz with physical height of about 33 feet (10 metres) or only 0.125 (one-eighth) in terms of wavelength.

Although having a very small 'gain' factor by virtue of the earth beneath acting as a 'plane reflector', each pattern is virtually

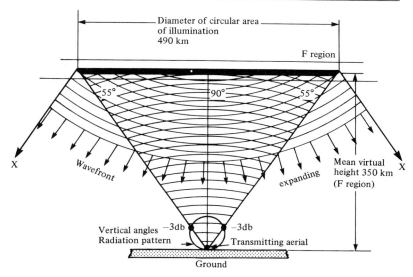

Figure 63 *Vertical angle radiation field from the aerial, as in Figure 62, expands as it travels toward the F region to produce a circular illumination area with a diameter of 490 kilometres*

circular. Illustration can only show flat patterns but together these indicate that if the radiation pattern could be shown in 'solid' form it would be 'spherical'. Ionospheric propagation at this frequency is via the F region and as the radiation travels upward it 'expands', as already described, and in this case conically as shown in Figure 63, to provide a fairly large area of radio frequency 'illumination' on reaching the F region.

It is quite easy to obtain approximation of the area of 'illumination' produced by the radiation when it meets the F region by using the angles from the − 3 dB points of the radiation pattern. There will of course be useful radiation at lower angles that would make the area of illumination larger but again the use of the − 3 dB points makes illustration easier. From this we can in any case get a reasonably good idea of the ground coverage by reflected and/or refracted signals.

Figure 64 shows a view that might be obtained if one could look down from above the F region and see the radiation illuminating both the region and the earth beneath. This mode of propagation has been proved on both 3.5 and 7 MHz by using half-wave aerials for either frequency at a height of 0.125 of a wavelength

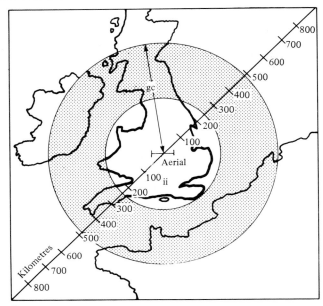

Key
ii   Ionospheric illumination
gc   Total ground coverage (see text)

Figure 64   *A view 'looking' down from above the F region. The area of illumination at the ionospheric region is (ii) and the area of ground coverage from the refracted wave is (ii + Gc) (see text)*

above ground. Knowing the radiation pattern of the aerial is the all-important factor, and although this can be distorted by using aerials bent into shapes other than dead straight, or by proximity of other aerials and conductors, e.g. local overhead telephone wires etc., such effects do not detract too much from the ionospheric omni-directional mode of propagation. In fact this mode is used by many radio amateurs without being aware of it, as the conditions with regard to the aerial height and frequency of operation comply more often than not. Much the same applies to omni-directional vertical aerials at low heights and physically short in terms of wavelength with respect to frequency of operation.

Note: The foregoing only applies if the critical frequency is at or above the frequency of operation, otherwise refraction will occur below the critical angle but still allow a wide area of coverage.

With horizontal aerials operated harmonically the effective

height will again be related to wavelength at the frequency of operation, i.e. as the frequency is increased the effective height of the aerial becomes greater. The number of main lobes in the horizontal radiation pattern also increase as the frequency is increased and maximum 'vertical angle' radiation from each lobe will be at lower angles with respect to ground. The 'omni-directional' effect described above would no longer apply except when such an aerial is operated as a half-wave.

Assessing ionospheric conditions

It is possible to get some idea if the critical frequency is at or above either 3.5 or 7 MHz and that 'omni-directional' ionospheric propagation is prevailing. If strong signals, S9 or over, can be received from stations a short distance away, say, 50 kilometres or 30 miles (other than by ground-wave propagation) and good signals are also being obtained from greater distances, up to 500 kilometres (300 miles) or more at the same time, then it is likely that the critical frequency is at, or above, whichever operating frequency is being used. This would rarely, if ever, apply to frequencies higher than 7 MHz.

Chordal mode propagation

So called chordal mode propagation has not been mentioned before but is believed to be a mode of propagation for DX operation around that portion of the earth away from the sun, i.e. where darkness exists over more or less the whole path of transmission. During the 'darkness' period the ionospheric F region virtual height increases and a wave meeting the region at an oblique angle may not be returned to earth in the normal way, but instead may be refracted from point to point, chordally, along the ionospheric region itself, as illustrated in Figure 65. The wave is finally returned to earth at a point where daylight again prevails and the F region is at a lower virtual height. Because a wave propagated by chordal mode is not returned to earth during propagation, it suffers very little attenuation. Some indication would be signals of exceptional strength from distances in the region of 12,000 miles.

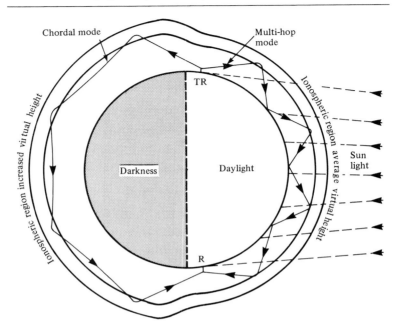

Figure 65 *Chordal mode ionospheric region propagation. Where the virtual height of the F region increases during the hours of darkness, a radiated wave will follow a 'chordal' path by being refracted along the region before being returned to earth (see text reference distance)*

Ionospheric propagation with vertical aerials

There is really little that can be said with regard to the use of vertical aerials except that by and large wave propagation via either the E or F regions is much the same as for horizontal aerials. In any case a change in polarization can take place with either form of aerial and again one may not always obtain the low vertical angle radiation so highly desirable for DX operation. Few radio amateurs could put up a full quarter-wave vertical aerial for the 1.8 MHz band but might manage one for 3.5 MHz (around 66 feet in height).

The higher frequency bands present little difficulty if one is prepared to use a radial ground plane and get the whole aerial as high as possible. There are of course 'all-in-one' multi-band inductively loaded aerials that lend themselves where space is limited, although some require a 'ground' system. The vertical angle radiation amplitude of such aerials is something of an unknown factor, as the author discovered by writing to numerous well-known manufacturers and dealers requesting such information, which none could supply. It may be generally accepted that with multi-band verticals maximum radiation in the vertical plane will be at fairly high angle, depending on the frequency band in use.

References

1 *The Amateur Radio Handbook*, RSGB, Edition 3, Feb. 62.
2 *The ARRL Antenna Handbook* (The American Radio Relay League 1974). (Later edition available RSGB.)
3 *HF Antennas for all Locations*, L. A. Moxon, RSGB.
4 'Broadside and Endfire Antenna Systems', *Practical Wireless*, F. C. Judd, Nov. 1985.
5 'Wires and Waves', *Practical Wireless Special Publication*, 1984.
6 *Beam Antenna Handbook*, 5th Edition, W. I. Orr, W6SAI (Radio Publication). (Available RSGB.)
7 *Antennas*, J. D. Kraus (McGraw-Hill).
8 'The Services Textbook of Radio', Vol. 5. *Transmission and Propagation* (HMSO 1958).

7 Radio waves: radiation

While this book is first and foremost concerned with the propagation of radio waves via the inonospheric regions, it would not be complete without including some notes on other modes of HF radio wave propagation, including the often used 'ground-wave' mode, as well as something of the basic principles of radiation.

Generally speaking, successful radio communication depends on the efficiency of the transmitting/receiving equipment, the aerial system(s) and personal operating skill. However, the aerial system(s) might be considered the most important link between the transmitting/receiving equipment and the medium of propagation. For example, any resonant aerial will radiate virtually all the power supplied to it but if the radiation travels in other than some desired direction, then it is wasted.

Radio wave radiation

Radiation

A radio wave is a combination of electric and magnetic fields and the energy created is divided between the two. If radio waves could be made to originate in 'free-space', from a point source, they would radiate outward in spheres of ever increasing area. The speed of expansion, equal to that at which radio waves travel in the atmosphere, is the same as the speed of light, because light is also an electro-magnetic wave.

In free-space the real speed at which radio waves travel is 299,793,077 metres (186,282,386 miles) per second. For general

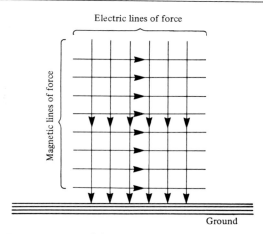

Figure 66 *Representation of the magnetic and electric fields of a vertically polarized plane wave. The arrows indicate the instantaneous directions of the fields for a wave travelling perpendicularly, i.e. toward the reader*

calculation these figures are rounded to 300,000,000 metres/s, or 186,000 miles/s respectively.

In a very short time a sphere expanding outward from a point source would become very large, and if visible observation were possible, any part of the wave would appear to be flat, just as the earth appears flat in one's immediate vicinity. When a radio wave is far enough from its source to be 'seemingly' flat, it is referred to as a 'plane wave'. Radio waves do in fact meet this condition having travelled only a short distance from a transmitting aerial. This is represented as lines of electric and magnetic force as illustrated in Figure 66.

As far as 'propagation' of a wave is concerned, the electric and magnetic lines are mutually perpendicular as the illustration indicates, but the wavefront is represented by the plane containing the crossed lines. A wave always travels in a direction perpendicular to the wavefront.

If a radio wave travels through a medium other than free-space the speed may not be 300×10^6 metres/s; there will be a reduction in speed depending on the nature of the medium through which the wave is travelling. With air as the medium the reduction in speed is generally small enough to be ignored.

With insulating materials the speed can be considerably slower and in otherwise good but closely spaced conductors (transmission lines) the speed may be so slow that opposing fields, set up by currents induced by a wave, may even cancel the wave out. This is also the reason for the so-called 'skin effect' in conductors carrying high frequency currents, and why metal boxes are used to screen one electrical circuit from another.

Wavelength and phase

The speed at which radio waves normally travel is so great that the time interval between the instant a wave leaves a transmitting aerial and when it reaches the point of reception is of little consequence, except in ionospheric sounding and similar 'pulse radar' systems. For instance it takes only about one-seventh of a second for a radio wave to travel the full circumference of the earth but 'time' becomes important in another way. The radiation of a radio wave is due to an alternating current flowing in a conductor, i.e. an aerial, which creates both the electric and magnetic fields. Alternating currents at radio frequencies range from a few thousand Hz to several million MHz. If we take as an example a frequency of 30 MHz, then one complete 'cycle' of the wave will have a duration of 1/30,000,000 of a second. Since the wave will normally travel at 300×10^6 metres/s, its front will have moved a distance of only 10 metres on completion of one cycle.

In other words the electro-magnetic field at 10 metres from an aerial is produced by the current that was flowing in the aerial one cycle (or period) earlier in time. At a steady frequency the duration of any one cycle of current is the same, i.e. each is a repetition of the one preceding.

Therefore the current in every following cycle will be the same. So also will be all the radiated fields that are produced. As the radiation expands outward from the aerial it becomes weaker, i.e. the amplitude of the wave suffers increasing attenuation as the distance from the aerial increases. However the 'cycle' time is not changed with respect to that at the instant at which it was generated. Therefore the 'phase' relationship of all the wavefronts travelling away from the aerial will remain the same.

The terms 'wavelength' and 'wavefront' can be defined more precisely, i.e. the wavelength is simply the distance between any two wavefronts, in phase, at any instant. This distance must however always be measured perpendicular to the wavefronts,

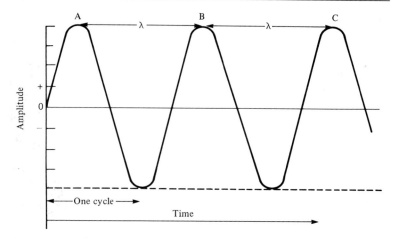

Figure 67 *The instantaneous amplitude of both fields (electric and magnetic) varies sinusoidually with time (see Figure 64). The distance between two points such as A and B, or B and C is the length of the wave (see text)*

i.e. along the line that represents the direction in which the wave is travelling. The length of a wave can be expressed as follows:

$$\lambda = \frac{v}{f}$$

where λ = wavelength, V = velocity of the wave, and f = the frequency of the recurrent cycles per second.

A more simplified expression is:

$$\lambda \text{ (metres)} = \frac{300}{f \text{ MHz}}$$

In simple terms 'phase' means 'time' and if the beginning and ending of each successive cycle occurs at exactly the same instant, then all the cycles are 'in-phase'. This is illustrated by Figure 67, in which the points A, B, and C are equidistant and represent the same 'time' interval between each of the cycles.

Figure 67 is the usual way of illustrating a sinusoidal current (or voltage) with time progressing to the right. The distance between A and B, or B and C, represents one wavelength and also indicates that the field intensity follows the sine curve with respect to both amplitude and polarity. However this is an 'instantaneous' representation. An actual radio wave travels rather like a wave created in water.

Field strength

The field strength of a radio wave is measured in terms of the voltage between two points on an electric line of force in the plane of the wavefront. Since the unit of length is the metre and the voltage is quite low at a distance, measurements are generally in micro-volts per metre. In amateur radio accurate field strength measurement is rarely ever necessary except when evaluating the performance of an aerial and for which fairly elaborate arrangements, as well as specialized equipment are required. It is common practice to measure *relative* field strength with simple equipment to determine whether an aerial is radiating, or to check for improvements, or otherwise, when some adjustment is made to a new or existing aerial.

Attenuation

In free- space the field strength of a wave decreases directly with distance from the source. For example, if the field strength a mile from the source is say, 100 μV/metre, it will be 50 μV/metre at two miles and 1 μV/metre at 100 miles and so on. In practice the rate of attenuation would be greater than this 'inverse law' implies. The wave would not be travelling in empty space all the time, even with ionospheric propagation. In this case attentuation occurs mainly when a radio wave makes contact with the earth after refraction from an ionospheric region. With ground-wave propagation the rate of attentuation is greater, as will be explained later.

Polarization

A radio wavefront as illustrated in Figure 66, may be said to be polarized in the direction of the electric lines of force. The polarization may be vertical because the electric field lines are vertical, i.e. perpendicular to earth. However, because the ground acts as a fairly good conductor, particularly at low frequencies, it is one of the laws of electro-magnetic wave propagation that the electric lines of force in contact with the surface of a conducting medium, must be perpendicular. However, over partially conducting ground there may be a forward 'tilt' to the wavefront which increases as the energy loss in the ground becomes greater.

It is usual to employ vertically polarized aerials for ground-wave propagation. If the electric lines of force are horizontal the polarization may be said to be horizontal also. In practice the polarization may be somewhere between horizontal and vertical and in many cases may not be fixed but continually rotating. When this occurs a radio wave is said to be elliptically polarized.

Ground-wave propagation

This term is normally used to describe a wave that is in actual contact with the ground along the whole path of travel. It is also used to define the propagation of a wave that travels directly between a transmitting aerial to a receiving aerial with only some of the wave making contact with the ground. This mode applies also to line-of-sight propagation at VHF and UHF for which the term 'ground-wave' is often wrongly used.

The surface wave

A radio wave that really does travel in contact with the surface of the earth should be called a 'surface wave' although this applies generally to the much lower frequency medium-wave broadcast band providing reception up to around 150/160 kilometres (100 miles or so) during the daytime. Night-time propagation distances are increased by refraction from the E region. For long-wave broadcast stations the day-time ground-wave distances can be much greater. At higher frequencies however, the distances that can be covered are much shorter and become less and less as the frequency of operation increases as shown in the graph Figure 68. Ground-wave propagation is frequently used for the 1.8 and 3.5 MHz amateur bands and with CB radio, ground-wave propagation as high as 27 MHz has become necessary. There has also been a trend recently for radio amateurs to use the allocated 28 MHz band for ground-wave propagated FM transmissions. On both these bands longer distances are often covered by propagation via sporadic E cloud formations, particularly during the summer months.

Ideally, the polarization of radiation for strictly ground-wave working should be vertical and this also applies to reception, i.e.

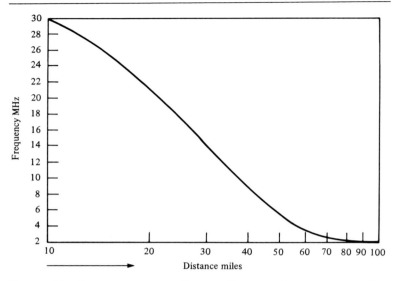

Figure 68 *Frequency versus distance for ground-wave propagation. Example (line) shows how limited the ground range is at 27 MHz. Approximately the same for 28 MHz*

the receiving aerial should be vertical, although normally a common aerial is used for both transmission and reception.

The space wave

This applies strictly to VHF and UHF line-of-sight propagation where the transmission normally travels directly between the points of transmission and reception. However the wave from a VHF/UHF transmitting aerial may well come into contact with ground, the angle of refraction (from the ground) being equal to the angle of incidence. In this case the direct and indirect waves can arrive at the point of reception either in, or out of phase, as shown in Figure 69. This can also apply to much lower frequencies e.g., 27 MHz (CB) and the 28/30 MHz amateur band.

Propagation from vertical aerials

At one time most mobile operation over short distances was carried out on the 1.8 MHz band. Of necessity aerials used for

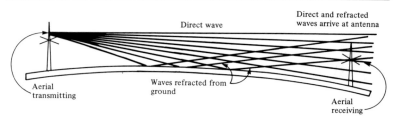

Figure 69 *Path of a direct wave, aerial to aerial, and path of the same wave, refracted from ground, arriving at the receiving aerial. The refracted, or indirect wave, could arrive in or out of phase with the direct wave*

mobile operation were very short in length with respect to wavelength being inductively loaded to achieve resonance. For fixed station operation the aerials used may have been either horizontal or vertical, mostly the former. However with short vertical aerials having a maximum height of a quarter wavelength the pattern for radiaton at vertical angles will be similar to that shown in Figure 70. Such aerials would otherwise be omni-directional.

As the height of a vertical aerial is increased the vertical angle radiation pattern tends to flatten out with a resultant increase in energy along the ground but a decrease at high angles. However, few radio amateurs could put up a full quarter wave aerial for home station operation on the 1.8 MHz band, or possibly even for the 3.5 MHz band, so a compromise usually has to be made by using a physically short aerial with inductive loading. In this case the aerial as a whole becomes less efficient and the vertical angle radiation occurs at much higher angles with consequently less radiation along a line parallel to ground. With vertical aerials at, or approaching a quarter wavelength in physical height, there is always some attenuation due to ground losses at very low angles.

Conclusion

Except for the cases mentioned, ground-wave propagation is little used these days by radio amateurs. If required, adequate ground-wave coverage can be obtained with a more or less conventional horizontal quarter or half-wave aerial as high as possible above ground, particularly for the lower frequency bands, 1.8 and

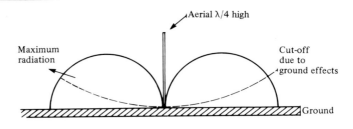

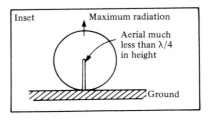

Figure 70   *Theoretical radiation pattern of vertical angle radiation from omnidirectional aerial a quarter wavelength high.* Inset: *The effect on the vertical angle radiation when a vertical aerial is much less than a quarter-wavelength high*

3.5 MHz. Such aerials will in any case provide good coverage with ionospheric propagation. As an example, even with a relatively low height aerial (10 to 12 metres above ground) operating as a horizontal half-wave on 3.5 MHz and with suitable ionospheric 'conditions', it is not unusual to work good DX, even to places as far away as New Zealand, the USA and Canada etc.

References

1 *HF Antennas for all Locations*, L. A. Moxon (RSGB Publication).
2 *Out of Thin Air*, P.W. Publishing Ltd.
3 'Ground Wave Propagation at 1.8 MHz', *RSGB Bulletin*, F. C. Judd, Dec. 1960.
4 *Radio, TV & Audio Technical Reference Book*, S. W. Amos (Heinemann Newnes).

8 Ionospheric (F region) propagation data

The data sheets consist of (a) average critical frequencies for the United Kingdom of Great Britain, covering the northern hemisphere, and (b) for Port Stanley in the Falkland Islands, covering the southern hemisphere.

In addition other data sheets are included which will provide the MUF for any of the critical frequencies listed, as well as the first 'hop' distance, provided the approximate vertical angle of radiation from the aerial in use is known.

The critical frequency tables can be adapted for other portions of the world by taking the time differences into account (relative to GMT) to obtain a reasonable approximation of critical frequencies for a 24-hour period based on the usual 12 noon (midday peak) for local time.

Instructions for use

1. Find critical frequency appropriate for time of day (GMT or local) and for summer or winter, sunspot solar cycle minimum or maximum, listed in tables as 1, 2, 3 or 4. *Note*: Nearest hour and critical frequency will suffice.
2. Locate MUF related to critical frequency (or nearest to it).
3. Under column 'ELEV', 0 to 90 degrees, in appropriate data sheets, A, B or C, select vertical angle of maximum radiation from aerial (known or estimated).
4. See how MUF relates to this and critical frequency.
5. Amateur band to be used must be equal to, or a little below the MUF.
6. The first hop distance will found in the column adjacent to 'ELEV' (degrees) *on the same line as the appropriate MUF.*

7 The first hop distances take into account the curvature of the surface of the earth and are based on a mean F region virtual height of 300 kilometres.

8 The number of hops after the first will depend on ionospheric conditions and ground absorption along the path of propagation and therefore determine the distance over which satisfactory communication can be maintained.

9 UK summer and winter periods. These can be taken as – summer – April to October, winter – October to April.

10 *Example.* Time – winter, solar sunspot maximum at 1100 hours GMT. For critical frequency, UK data column 4, the nearest frequency would be 11.3 MHz (1000 hours gives 10.2 and 1200 hours 12.5 MHz).

Your aerial has vertical angle of maximum radiation at 30 degrees and is a rotatable beam for the 21 MHz band only. The MUF's data sheet (b) gives critical frequency as either 11 or 11.5. Take 11.0 MHz. This gives MUF of either 17.9 or 20.4 MHz with ELEV of either 34 or 28 degrees respectively. With your aerial providing vertical angle maximum radiation at 30 degrees your first hop distance is between 800 and 1000 kilometres. The MUF is a bit low but some contact on that band should be possible. On the other hand, if the critical frequency had been 12.5 MHz, the MUF would have been in the region of 21 MHz. In other words in about another hour conditions would have been better.

Remember that vertical angle radiation from an aerial will be spread either side of the angle of maximum, so taking the – 3 dB points provides what might be called useful radiation over a wider range of vertical angles. For example, the – 3 dB point of the main lobe, nearest to ground, may be a considerable number of degrees *lower* than maximum, which gives more leeway in relation to MUF and first hop distance. The use of the data can therefore provide a broader aspect than may at first be realized.

The following is a table, kilometres to miles, relating to the hop distances given in data sheets (a), (b) and (c).

Miles = kilometres × 0.6124
Kilometres to miles

Kilometres	Miles		
100	61.2	2000	1224.8
200	122.5	2100	1286
300	183.7	2200	1347.3
400	245	2300	1408.5
500	306.2	2400	1469.8
600	367.4	2500	1531
700	428.7	2600	1592.2
800	489.9	2700	1653.5
900	551.2	2800	1714.7
1000	612.4	2900	1776
1100	673.6	3000	1837.2
1200	734.9	3100	1898.4
1300	796.1	3200	1959.7
1400	857.4	3300	2020.9
1500	918.6	3400	2082.2
1600	979.8	3500	2143.4
1700	1041.1	3600	2204.6
1800	1102.3	3700	2265.9
1900	1163.6	3800	2327.1
		3900	2388.4
		4000	2449.6

F Region. Critical Frequencies. UK.

Time GMT						Noon					Time GMT	
0000	0200	0400	0600	0800	1000	1200	1400	1600	1800	2000	2200	2400

1 Critical frequencies MHz. Summer sunspot minimum

3.5	2.3	2.5	3.5	4.4	4.5	4.5	4.5	4.6	5.0	4.8	4.0	3.5

2 Critical frequencies MHz. Summer sunspot maximum

6.0	5.2	5.0	6.1	7.2	7.6	7.1	7.0	7.5	8.2	8.5	8.3	6.0

Time GMT						Noon					Time GMT	
0000	0200	0400	0600	0800	1000	1200	1400	1600	1800	2000	2200	2400

3 Critical frequencies MHz. Summer sunspot minimum

2.5	3.4	3.9	4.1	5.9	7.3	7.3	5.9	4.0	2.9	2.7	2.6	2.5

4 Critical frequencies MHz. Winter sunspot maximum

4.0	3.8	3.5	3.6	6.2	10.2	12.5	12.2	12.1	8.5	6.5	5.3	4.0

Applies 24 hours. Based on noon peak readings. Slough Ionosonde, Berks.
Courtesy of Rutherford Appleton Laboratory. Chilton. Oxfordshire.

F region critical frequencies. Port Stanley.

Time local GMT − 4 hours				Noon						Time local		
0000	0200	0400	0600	0800	1000	1200	1400	1600	1800	2000	2200	2400

1   Critical frequencies MHz. Summer sunspot minimum

2.3	2.3	2.3	2.0	4.0	4.4	5.2	4.8	4.7	2.7	2.5	2.4	2.3

2   Critical frequencies MHz. Summer sunspot maximum

3.0	3.0	3.0	2.8	6.5	7.4	8.6	7.7	6.7	4.4	2.9	2.9	3.0

Time local				Noon						Time local		
0000	0200	0400	0600	0800	1000	1200	1400	1600	1800	2000	2200	2400

3   Critical frequencies MHz. Winter sunspot minimum

3.0	3.0	3.1	2.8	5.4	6.5	7.0	6.2	5.5	4.0	3.3	3.2	3.0

4   Critical frequencies MHz. Winter sunspot maximum

4.8	4.6	4.6	4.6	9.4	12.2	13.4	11.7	9.8	7.6	2.9	2.9	3.0

Applies 24 hours. Based on noon peak readings. Port Stanley. Falkland Islands.
Note: Times above are local. Add 4 hours for GMT. Courtesy R.A Lab. Oxon.

MUFs versus Range and Elevation
for a given ionospheric height and a range of critical frequencies

(a) Ionospheric heights, km 300

		Critical Frequency MHz*									
kms	Elev	2.5	3	3.5	4	4.5	5	5.5	6	6.5	7
0	90	2.5	3	3.5	4	4.5	5	5.5	6	6.5	7
200	71	2.6	3.2	3.7	4.2	4.7	5.3	5.8	6.3	6.8	7.4
400	55	3	3.6	4.2	4.8	5.4	6	6.6	7.2	7.8	8.4
600	43	3.5	4.2	4.9	5.6	6.3	7	7.7	8.4	9.1	9.8
800	34	4.1	4.9	5.7	6.5	7.3	8.1	8.9	9.7	10.6	11.4
1000	28	4.6	5.6	6.5	7.4	8.3	9.3	10.2	11.1	12.1	13
1200	23	5.2	6.2	7.3	8.3	9.4	10.4	11.4	12.5	13.5	14.6
1400	20	5.7	6.9	8	9.2	10.3	11.5	12.6	13.8	14.9	16.1
1600	16	6.2	7.5	8.7	10	11.2	12.4	13.7	14.9	16.2	17.4
1800	14	6.7	8	9.3	10.7	12	13.3	14.6	16	17.3	18.6
2000	12	7	8.4	9.9	11.3	12.7	14.1	15.5	16.9	18.3	19.7
2200	10	7.4	8.8	10.3	11.8	13.3	14.7	16.2	17.7	19.2	20.6
2400	8	7.6	9.2	10.7	12.2	13.8	15.3	16.8	18.4	19.9	21.4
2600	7	7.9	9.5	11	12.6	14.2	15.8	17.3	18.9	20.5	22.1
2800	5	8.1	9.7	11.3	12.9	14.5	16.1	17.7	19.3	21	22.6
3000	4	8.2	9.8	11.5	13.1	14.8	16.4	18	19.7	21.3	23
3200	3	8.3	10	11.6	13.3	14.9	16.6	18.3	19.9	21.6	23.3
3400	2	8.4	10	11.7	13.4	15.1	16.7	18.4	20.1	21.8	23.4
3600	1	8.4	10.1	11.8	13.5	15.1	16.8	18.5	20.2	21.9	23.6
3800	0	8.4	10.1	11.8	13.5	15.2	16.9	18.5	20.2	21.9	23.6

(b) Ionospheric height, km *300*

Critical Frequency MHz*

kms	Elev	7.5	8	8.5	9	9.5	10	10.5	11	11.5	12
0	90	7.5	8	8.5	9	9.5	10	10.5	11	11.5	12
200	71	7.9	8.4	9	9.5	10	10.5	11.1	11.6	12.1	12.6
400	55	9	9.6	10.2	10.8	11.4	12	12.6	13.2	13.8	14.4
600	43	10.5	11.2	11.9	12.6	13.3	14	14.7	15.4	16.1	16.8
800	34	12.2	13	13.8	14.6	15.4	16.2	17	17.9	18.7	19.5
1000	28	13.9	14.8	15.8	16.7	17.6	18.6	19.5	20.4	21.3	22.3
1200	23	15.6	16.7	17.7	18.7	19.8	20.8	21.9	22.9	23.9	25
1400	20	17.2	18.4	19.5	20.6	21.8	22.9	24.1	25.2	26.4	27.5
1600	16	18.7	19.9	21.2	22.4	23.6	24.9	26.1	27.4	28.6	29.9
1800	14	20	21.3	22.6	24	25.3	26.6	28	29.3	30.6	32
2000	12	21.1	22.5	23.9	25.3	26.8	28.2	29.6	31	32.4	33.8
2200	10	22.1	23.6	25.1	26.5	28	29.5	31	32.4	33.9	35.4
2400	8	22.9	24.5	26	27.5	29.1	30.6	32.1	33.6	35.2	36.7
2600	7	23.6	25.2	26.8	28.4	29.9	31.5	33.1	34.7	36.2	37.8
2800	5	24.2	25.8	27.4	29	30.6	32.2	33.8	35.5	37.1	38.7
3000	4	24.6	26.2	27.9	29.5	31.2	32.8	34.4	36.1	37.7	39.4
3200	3	24.9	26.6	28.2	29.9	31.6	33.2	34.9	36.5	38.2	39.9
3400	2	25.1	26.8	28.5	30.1	31.8	33.5	35.2	36.8	38.5	40.2
3600	1	25.2	26.9	28.6	30.3	32	33.7	35.3	37	38.7	40.4
3800	0	25.3	27	28.7	30.4	32	33.7	35.4	37.1	38.8	40.5

* *Note:* Highest critical frequency ever recorded at Slough Ionosonde station (Rutherford Appleton Lab.) was 22 MHz during the maximum of sunspot cycle no. 21 in 1980.

MUFs versus Range and Elevation
for a given ionospheric height and a range of critical frequencies

(c) Ionospheric Height, km 300

Critical Frequency MHz*

kms	Elev	12.5	13	13.5	14	14.5	15	15.5	16	16.5	17
0	90	12.5	13	13.5	14	14.5	15	15.5	16	16.5	17
200	71	13.2	13.7	14.2	14.8	15.3	15.8	16.3	16.9	17.4	17.9
400	55	15	15.6	16.2	16.8	17.4	18	18.6	19.2	19.8	20.4
600	43	17.5	18.2	18.9	19.6	20.3	21	21.7	22.4	23.1	23.8
800	34	20.3	21.1	21.9	22.7	23.5	24.4	25.2	26	26.8	27.6
1000	28	23.2	24.1	25	26	26.9	27.8	28.8	29.7	30.6	31.5
1200	23	26	27.1	28.1	29.1	30.2	31.2	32.3	33.3	34.3	35.4
1400	20	28.7	29.8	31	32.1	33.3	34.4	35.6	36.7	37.8	39
1600	16	31.1	32.3	33.6	34.8	36.1	37.3	38.6	39.8	41.1	42.3
1800	14	33.3	34.6	35.9	37.3	38.6	39.9	41.3	42.6	43.9	45.3
2000	12	35.2	36.6	38	39.4	40.8	42.2	43.6	45.1	46.5	47.9
2200	10	36.8	38.3	39.8	41.3	42.7	44.2	45.7	47.2	48.6	50.1
2400	8	38.2	39.8	41.3	42.8	44.4	45.9	47.4	48.9	50.5	52
2600	7	39.4	41	42.5	44.1	45.7	47.3	48.8	50.4	52	53.6
2800	5	40.3	41.9	43.5	45.1	46.7	48.4	50	51.6	53.2	54.8
3000	4	41	42.6	44.3	45.9	47.6	49.2	50.8	52.5	54.1	55.8
3200	3	41.5	43.2	44.8	46.5	48.2	49.8	51.5	53.1	54.8	56.5
3400	2	41.9	43.5	45.2	46.9	48.6	50.2	51.9	53.6	55.3	56.9
3600	1	42.1	43.8	45.4	47.1	48.8	50.5	52.2	53.9	55.5	57.2
3800	0	42.2	43.8	45.5	47.2	48.9	50.6	52.3	54	55.6	57.3

* Average highest for winter period sunspot maximum is 12–14 MHz.

Sporadic E (Es) data

The formation of sporadic E clouds has been dealt with in other parts of this book.

Radio amateurs have no means of knowing immediately when a sporadic E event is occurring, or has occurred, except that conditions on certain frequency bands may indicate that sporadic E is providing propagation. There is no set time of day and no specific periodicity, e.g. once in every so many days. Sporadic E occurs quite randomly, mostly during the summer months, although at times during the winter months as well.

Observations carried out by the author over a period of some three years, and compared with those made by the Rutherford Appleton Laboratory, revealed that sporadic E may occur in one part of the country but not in another a relatively short distance away.

The occurrence of sporadic E is rather like that of certain

tropospheric conditions that allow long distance communication on VHF and UHF, somewhat random, although the onset of tropospheric 'lift' conditions can often be anticipated from the way in which changes in barometric readings occur.

Data

The data that follows stems from real observations by pulse sounding and gives some idea of just how random Es events can be. The data covers the summer months, May, June, July and August, of 1985 and applies only to observations carried out at the location given.

Sporadic E (Es) observations for year 1985.
Note: Total hours per month are in decimal format, i.e. 0.1 hours = 6 minutes, Times of observations are in 24-hour time GMT.
Computer Code. ION ES.

Sporadic E (Es) observations 1985

Date	1	2	3	4	5	6	7
Month	Duration of hours each day						
May	0.0						
June	0.1	1.5	0.0	0.1	0.1	2.0	1.0
July	0.1	0.5		nil		0.2	0.1
August				nil			
Total hrs	0.2	2.0	0.0	0.1	0.1	2.2	1.1
Observed time of beginning at	all hours GMT						
May							
June	1115	0815		1020	0830	1043	0840
July	1015	1110				1150	1030
August							

Summer months only as listed
G9BTN Cantley, Norfolk.

Sporadic E (Es) observations 1985

Date	8	9	10	11	12	13	14
Month	Duration of hours each day						
May			nil				
June	0.1			nil			4.1
July			1.2				
August				nil			
Total hrs	0.1	0.0	1.2	0.0	0.0	0.0	4.1
Observed time beginning at	all hours GMT						
May							
June	0655						1150
July			1030				
August							

Summer months as listed.
G9BTN Cantley, Norfolk.

Sporadic E (Es) Observations 1985.

Date	15	16	17	18	19	20	21
Month	Duration of hours each day						
May	0.1			nil			
June		F Layer	nil	0.1	2.0		0.8
July							
August				nil			
Total hours	0.1	0.0	0.0	0.1	2.0	0.0	0.8
Observed time Beginning at	all hours GMT						
May	1115						
June				0717	0700		1010
July							
August							

Summer months as listed.
G9BTN Cantley, Norfolk.

Sporadic E (Es) observations 1985.

Date	22	23	24	25	26	27	28
Month	Duration of hours each day						
May		nil					0.2
June		nil			0.1		nil
July				nil			
August		2.0		nil			
Total hours	2.0	0.0	0.0	0.0	0.0	0.1	0.0	0.2

Observed time
Beginning at   all hours GMT

May						1056
June				1100		
July						
August	1130					

Summer months as listed.
G9BTN Cantley, Norfolk.

Sporadic E (Es) observations 1985.

Date	28	29	30	31	totals
Month	Durations hours				
May	nil				0.3
June	nil				12.0
July	nil				2.1
August					Month totals
Total hours	0.0	0.0	0.0	0.0	16.4
					Year total hours

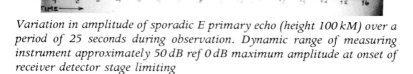

Variation in amplitude of sporadic E primary echo (height 100 kM) over a period of 25 seconds during observation. Dynamic range of measuring instrument approximately 50 dB ref 0 dB maximum amplitude at onset of receiver detector stage limiting

Question and answer data

Q Although the F region average virtual height is between 300 and 350 kilometres observations show that the height can increase to 450 to 480 kilometres. Does the whole region move up and down?

A The reflected frequency is proportional to the square root of the electron density ($f \propto \sqrt{N}$). As the electron density increases with height (up to a maximum) and varies with time of day and season, heights indicated by echo sounding will vary. The whole region does move up at night and its thickness varies, often from hour to hour.

Q What determines the 'virtual' height from which a pulsed radio wave will be reflected?

A The pulse will be reflected from the height at which the electron density *N* satisfies the $f \propto \sqrt{N}$ relationship.

Q Is fading of normal radio waves or, in the case of pulse sounding, amplitude variation of the returned echo, due to low denisty ionization?

A Fading is due mainly to the movement of irregularities in the ionosphere. Weak pulse transmission echoes and normal radio signals result from absorption, either in the D region, or in the vicinity of the height of maximum electron concentration. Low electron density will also produce a low critical frequency.

Q Signals disappear completely for varying periods. Could this be due to D region absorption?

A From time to time a solar flare will produce a large increase in electron density in the D region, and consequently signals will be totally absorbed before reaching the E and F regions. This applies to signals travelling up to a region, or reflected/refracted from above the D region.

Q Does the F region have a finite thickness or does this vary?

A The F region thickness is of the order 100 to 200 kilometres and varies with time of day and season. The E region and sporadic clouds are 1 to 2 kilometres thick.

Q Are the E or F regions affected by weather conditions in the normal atmosphere?

A This point is dealt with in Chapter 4. Otherwise and so far as is known, earth weather conditions do not affect the ionospheric regions.

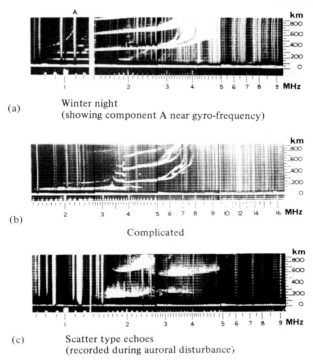

(a) Winter night
(showing component A near gyro-frequency)

(b) Complicated

(c) Scatter type echoes
(recorded during auroral disturbance)

Figure 71   *Three complex ionograms as described in detail in Q and A text*

Q What is the Gyro frequency?

A The Gyro frequency is the frequency of rotation of the electrons about the direction of the earth's magnetic field in the ionosphere. It is directly proportional to the magnitude of the field and for Slough (Ionosonde station) the value is 1.2 MHz. The separation of the critical frequencies of the ordinary and extraordinary components is half the Gyro frequency, i.e. 0.6 MHz.

Q Does the Gyro frequency vary?

A The extraordinary component is heavily absorbed and retarded around the Gyro frequency and is rarely seen at the Slough Ionosonde station below 1.6 MHz. In Figure 71(a) it is present between 0.8 and 1.1 MHz on a night-time ionogram when both absorption and interference were extremely low. The frequency spread of echoes from the F region is often recorded during a winter night.

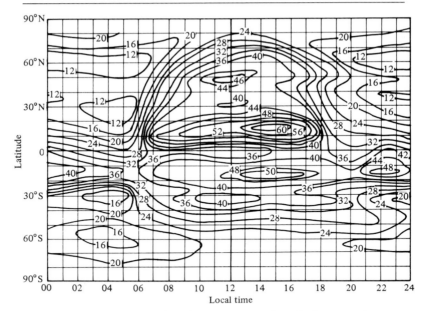

Figure 72   *Typical MUF distribution map as described in Q and A text*

Q What is a 'complicated' ionogram?

A This is illustrated in Figure 71(b). The complex pattern above 6 MHz is produced by tilts in the electron density contours giving rise to off-vertical returns.

Q What are 'scatter' type echoes?

A These are shown in the ionogram Figure 71(c). During a severe magnetic storm the auroral ionosphere moves towards the equator. The echo traces become spread and complex, with a combination of vertical and oblique returns. Auroral type sporadic E is present from 100 to 400 kilometres. Although the overhead F region is penetrated at 2.5 MHz, oblique reflections continue up to 5.0 MHz.

Q What is an MUF distribution map?

A These are maps that show how the MUF for transmissions from a given site over distances of 4000 kilometres (2500 miles) and using refraction from the F region, varies during a 24-hour period (local time). Such maps change throughout the year. The example, as in Figure 72 is typical but these maps can apply to transmitter sites on any latitude.

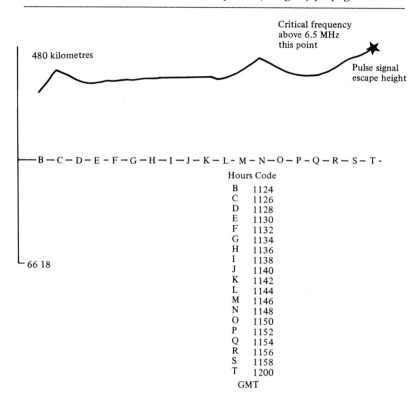

Figure 73 *Computer readout showing short time taken for F region ionization intensity to decrease sufficiently to allow 90 degree incident pulse transmission to penetrate region when critical frequency exceeded 6.5 MHz*

Q How quickly can the F region critical frequency change?

A This is illustrated by a computer readout, Figure 73. The critical frequency has changed from about 6 MHz at an F region virtual height of 300 kilometres (left-hand side of graph) to a new critical frequency (6.5 MHz) with the virtual height increased to 480 kilometres. Beyond this point the pulse transmissions used to plot the graph have reached the penetration frequency at above 6.5 MHz. The time taken for this to occur was 36 minutes.

Q How is the MUF, LUF and critical frequency related to the sunspot number?

A The graphs, Figure 74, illustrate this. The critical frequency fo

141

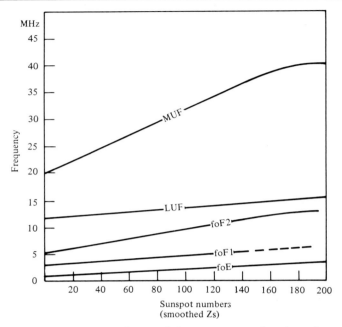

Figure 74   *MUF, LUF and critical frequency as a function of sunspot number. (Courtesy of USA Department NOAA)*

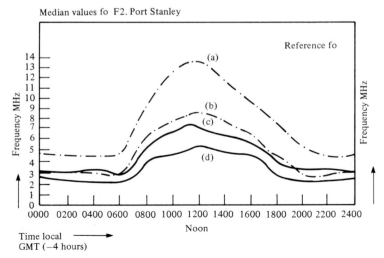

Figure 75   *Average critical frequencies for summer and winter, solar cycle sunspot maximum and minimum. Falkland Islands. (Courtesy Rutherford Appleton Laboratory, Oxfordshire)*

F2 and the MUF flatten out at around a smoothed sunspot number of 150 because the F2 region electron density has reached a saturation point. Critical frequency fo Fl is shown (dashed line) above the SSN because it tends to be masked by the F2 region at high sunspot numbers. (Graphs courtesy USA Department National Oceanic and Atmospheric Administration, Boulder, Colorado.)

Q Are the median critical frequencies for the southern hemisphere mid-latitudes very much different from those applying to the northern hemisphere?

A Not greatly, as the graphs in Figure 75 show. (a) Winter, solar cycle maximum. (b) Summer, solar cycle minimum. (c) Winter, solar cycle maximum. (d) Summer, solar cycle minimum. See also ionospheric (F region) propagation data on page 129 and figure 31, Chapter 3.

The end of solar cycle no. 21

The prediction of this was dealt with in Chapter 3, but since the time it was produced some months have elapsed. Continued observations and the application of a computer, indicate that this cycle has possibly ended a few months before the predicted time, and that the new cycle will be on an 'upward trend' by the time this book is published. If this prediction proves to be correct it will be good news for amateur radio HF band operators and a fitting end to this book, hence the inclusion of the data sheets, Figure 76(a) and (b). These cover the whole of 1985 and up to the end of March 1986 and show average 'daily' hours during which the F region critical frequency (fo) was at, or above 6.5 MHz.

The first part of the curve, covering the end of the winter period 1985, January, February and March, shows a relatively low level by comparison with that for the same months in 1986 where the level is beginning to rise after the 'peak' of the winter period during October and November. This is fairly significant because if the solar cycle no. 21 had NOT reached minimum, the trend would have been a 'fall' in the fo F2 6.5 MHz observations. The second data sheet (b) gives the average daily hours for each day of the 15 months listed, as well as related percentages. For the first three months of 1986 the percentages are considerably greater than for those of the first three months of 1985.

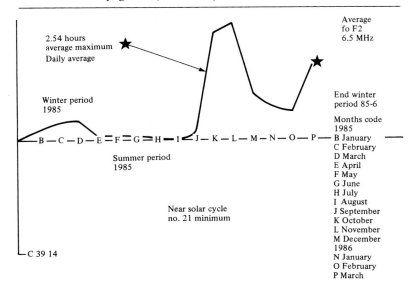

Information

Average fo F2 6.5 MHz*

Column		Average daily hours *	Percentage
B	Jan.	0.23	2.26
C	Feb.	0.35	3.45
D	Mar.	0.43	4.24
E	Apr.	0.10	0.98
F	May	0.10	0.98
G	June	0.09	0.88
H	July	0.00	0.00
I	Aug.	0.00	0.00
J	Sept.	0.07	0.69
K	Oct.	2.33	22.97
L	Nov.	2.54	25.04
M	Dec.	0.98	9.66
N	Jan.	0.70	6.90
O	Feb.	0.62	6.11
P	Mar.	1.60	15.77

100% = 10.14

Figure 76 *(a) Later but still probable prediction for end of solar cycle no. 21, earlier than originally predicted, (computer analysis). (b) Information readout. Percentage rise for first three months of 1986 higher than for same months 1985*

Continued observations will eventually reveal how close this prediction really is, although there will be the usual 'summer' fall before the winter period of 1986, when it is hoped that the 'upward trend' will continue through the following years.

Index

American OTHR, 83–104
Angle of incidence, 112
Anomalies, ionospheric, 67
Antarctica, ionospherics and ice, 82
Appleton, E. V., 7
    tribute to, 11
Appleton pulse technique, 17
Attenuation, radio waves, 124

Back scatter, 72
Breit pulse technique, 6
British over the horizon radar, 103

Chordal mode propagation, 117
Critical frequency:
    general, 10, 41, 53, 60
    solar cycle, 58, 59, 142

Data, general, 129–37
D region, 38
D region scatter, 71

Early experiments, ionospherics, 5, 6
Earth weather and ionospherics, 21
Earth magnetic field, effect, 37
E region, 38
E and F region, discovery, 9
Eleven-year solar cycle, 45, 54, 79
Es (Sporadic E), 38, 134

Fading, radio waves, 70
Field strength, radio waves, 124
Fo and Fx components, 37
F region, 39, 129
F region scatter, 72–3

Great circle paths, 68
Ground-wave attenuation, 126
Ground-wave propagation, 125
Ground-wave reflection factor, 110
Gyro frequency, 139

Heaviside layer, 5
Hop distances, 111–13

Ionograms, 31, 36, 139, 140
Ionosonde, 27–30
Ionospheric changes, 70
    echoes, 18
    electron density, 19–21
    omni-directional propagation, 114–16
    reflecting media, 61, 62
    region, heights, 21
    regions, function, 1, 19, 37
    region parameters, 26
    region variations, 61
    storms, 77

Kennelly-heaviside layer, 7

Lowest usuable frequency, 42, 43

Magnetoionic splitting, 35
Magnetoionic theory, 9
M and N modes, propagation,
    77, 78
Marconi. G., 11
Maunder minimum, 46, 47
McNish-Lincoln prediction, 56–8
Meteor trails, 75
MUF (maxium usuable
    frequency), 42
    data, 132, 140
Multiple reflections,
    Ionospherics, 34

N and M mode propagation, 77,
    78

Observation (sunspots), 47, 48
One-way transmission paths, 69
Origin, sunspot numbers, 63, 64
Over the horizon radar:
    American Conus B, 83
    Russian Woodpecker, 97
    British Marconi, 103

Questions and Answers, 138–43

Radio waves, radiation, 120
Rayleigh, diffraction theory, 3
Reflecting medium, 5
Refraction ionospheric, 22–4
Region height v transmission
    distance, 41

Scatter propagation, 71–3
SID (sudden ionospheric
    disturbance), 77
Skip distance, 39, 40
Single frequency ionospheric
    sounding, 33
Solar flares, 49
Solar flux, 51
Solar radiation, 51, 52
Solar sunspot cycles, 44–8
Space wave, 126
Space shuttle, ionospheric
    disturbance, 81
Split echoes, 34
Sporadic E (Es), 38, 73, 74, 134
Spurious directivity, 69
Solar cycle no. 21, 50, 57, 143
Sunspot numbers, 51, 65
Sunspot observation, 47, 48

Transmitting aerials and
    propagation, 105
Trans-equatorial openings, 68
Tuve pulse technique, 6

Vertical aerials, propagation, 118
Virtual height, ionospheric
    regions, 41

Wavelength and phase,
    propagation, 122
Weather and ionospherics, 79
Wireless echoes, early work, 14
Wolf number, sunspot counts,
    49, 63, 74